The Adventures of Scaredy Cat

A Family Storybook

Bernard Foster

Prayers by David Gatward
Illustrated by Jennifer Carter

Kevin
Mayhew

First published in 1998 by
KEVIN MAYHEW LTD
Rattlesden
Bury St Edmunds
Suffolk IP30 0SZ

0 1 2 3 4 5 6 7 8 9

ISBN 1 84003 098 4
Catalogue No 1500171

Cover by Jennifer Carter
Edited by David Gatward
Typesetting by Louise Selfe
Printed and bound in Great Britain

CONTENTS

FOREWORD

Twenty-five years' experience as a primary school teacher taught me many things, and one of the most important was that younger children will often learn and respond best through the medium of story telling. They have the capacity to link themselves with the characters in the story, and learn from the experiences of those characters.

When faced with providing something for the children of my church as part of a Children's Spot in the morning services, I began to think of how I could teach them by using stories. On this basis, *Scaredy Cat* was born shortly afterwards.

One day, when I was thinking about another character for the stories, I glanced up to the roof of our church and spotted two carved stone angels looking down over the people. The Stone Angel was thus included in the stories.

As the stories developed and the children began to ask for more, I was very surprised when this was quickly followed by a similar request from the adult members of the congregation, who seemed to appreciate them even more! This book contains many of the stories told to the children in my church.

It is my prayer that they will enable you to teach effectively some of the great Christian truths to young and old alike, and that through them, many will come to know him, whom to know is life indeed.

BERNARD FOSTER

INTRODUCING SCAREDY CAT

Scaredy Cat is found, and becomes a new member of the family.

One day the Rev James Brown woke up and went downstairs to put on the kettle to make some tea for himself and his wife. He did this every morning, whilst the two children, Susan and David, usually had a glass of orange juice. The Brown family consisted of father, a rather tall, thin man with fair hair, Mrs Brown who was short and rather plump, and their two children. Susan was a girl of nine years of age, and was tall and thin with the same fair hair as her father. David was seven years old, much shorter but quite plump, just like his mother.

Mr Brown heard an early morning knocking on the front door of the vicarage. Strolling along the hall, he grasped the door handle and pulled the old door open. As he expected, it was the paper boy with his newspapers, which he handed to the vicar. But then the boy pointed to the step and said, 'You've got a strange-looking parcel too, and it seems to be moving!'

Mr Brown looked down and spotted a bundle of rags on the doorstep. It did indeed seem to be moving slightly. Bending down, he carefully unwrapped the rags around the bundle and to his astonishment there sat a small, almost black cat, probably only a few weeks old. 'Miaow,' said the cat miserably. The vicar carefully picked it up. 'You poor thing,' said the vicar, as the cat sat in his arms, trembling as much with fear as with the cold morning air. 'Somebody must have left you wrapped up on the doorstep during the night.'

He carefully carried the rag bundle with the cat in it into the vicarage, and through the hall and into the kitchen.

'Look what has been left on our doorstep,' said Mr Brown to his wife and the children, who all gathered around in amazement. 'The poor little thing is very frightened, and won't stop trembling. What a terrible way to treat a cat.'

Very quickly the cat was settled down on the floor in front of a fire, with a saucer of milk. Everyone noticed that he was a very fine looking cat, but still very frightened. Every time someone moved or if there was a noise like a door being closed, the cat would run for its life under the nearest chair, and hide, almost as though his life depended on it.

'I wonder what we can do with him,' thought Mr Brown out loud. 'I suppose he will have to stay here until we can find someone who would like a rather frightened black cat.'

The two children were very certain about what to do with the cat. 'Oh, please,' they pleaded, 'can we keep him? He's a lovely kitten and he'd love living here. We'll take care of him and feed him.'

Mr and Mrs Brown were not at all sure of this. 'He will have to be left on his own for a long time each day, because

you will be at school and we will both be out taking services or visiting in the parish. This is a very busy house!'
said Mrs Brown. But the children continued to plead for
him, and eventually, the little frightened face hiding under
the chair won them over. It was agreed that the cat should
stay at the vicarage.

After a few weeks around the house he seemed much
more at home and would go out into the large garden. He
also seemed very good at getting into mischief, playing
with balls of wool and sometimes getting lost. So it was
that the cat settled down to life in the vicarage, much to
the delight of Susan and David.

Very slowly the cat seemed to grow less frightened of
everybody and everything. He no longer ran away and hid
under the chair. 'He must have been treated really badly
when he was young,' said Mr Brown. 'He was so scared
when he arrived here, but just look at him now!' Then he
had an idea. 'I know, because he was so frightened when
he first came, we will call him Scaredy Cat!'

From that day on, Scaredy Cat became the vicarage cat.
He became used to lots of visitors to the vicarage, and to
Mr Brown and his wife going out to attend meetings, and
the children being at school during the week. But on Sun-
days they all used to go to the big church next door, and
Scaredy Cat started to wonder what they did there.

Think about . . .

Is there anyone new in your school or street? How do you think they feel? Perhaps you have just moved to a new place? How do you feel?

Pray about . . .

Dear God,
    it can't be easy
    moving to a new place,
    a new school.

Lots of new faces.
Lots of strange places.

You have to meet
    new people
    and often leave behind
    those you love.

I pray, Lord,
    for all those people
    who are moving
    to a new place.

Help them to be happy, God.

Amen.

Exploring

Scaredy Cat makes a friend, and hears about our Heavenly Father for the first time.

Being a young cat, and very curious, Scaredy Cat used to go exploring each day, soon learning his way around the vicarage. It was quite an old building, with lots of rooms, some of which were never used. Scaredy Cat spent most of his time in the large, warm kitchen, where he used to sleep in a box under the large kitchen table. Mrs Brown spent a lot of her time in the kitchen too, keeping him company. There was also a large living room, which served as a dining room where all the family met for their meals. There was another room, called the study. This was where Mr Brown spent most of his time working, and often where he used to talk to people. Up the stairs there seemed to be quite a lot of bedrooms, but Scaredy Cat didn't go into the study or up the stairs very often.

Outside, at the back of the house, was a lovely large garden, with a long lawn where Scaredy Cat could play, and flower beds everywhere. At the end of the garden were a large number of bushes, which sometimes had flowers on them, and a few large trees. The house on one side of the vicarage had some children living there, and at the house at the bottom of the garden there lived another cat, called Ginger Tom by the family who lived there. Scaredy Cat didn't go much further than that for quite a long time after he arrived at the vicarage.

On the other side of the vicarage was the church. Every Sunday, and often during the week, Mr and Mrs Brown and Susan and David would go into the church, where Scaredy Cat could hear them singing.

One Sunday, he wandered into the church and sat down to listen to the service, and Mr Brown who was preaching.

He enjoyed it so much that he began to go into the church for every service, and all the people began to grow quite fond of their regular little visitor. He even joined in their singing occasionally! Unfortunately, though he could understand what everyone was saying (cats are very clever, you know!) all he could say was 'Miaow'!

What he liked to do most of all was to go into the church during the week, when there were no services, and just sit by himself. He liked the peace and quiet of the church, though he always made sure that he avoided the cleaners each week, who always complained that he left hairs everywhere, and muddy paw prints!

One day he sat looking around him in the church. There were dozens of pews where the people would sit, and some nice warm radiators, where he always sat. The church had some beautifully carved wooden furniture, and a large pulpit where Mr Brown usually stood to give his sermon. Scaredy Cat always listened carefully to what he said. He couldn't always understand what he said, but he tried to learn.

As he sat looking around him, he saw that the church had twelve stone pillars in the main part, six on each side, and the top of each pillar was carved into the shape of an angel, a stone angel. Scaredy Cat thought that they looked rather stern and stony-faced. All of them, that is, except for one, who seemed to have a softer face than the others, and even a suggestion of a smile on his lips.

As he sat looking at this stone angel, Scaredy Cat nearly jumped out of his skin. Surely the Stone Angel had winked his eye at him! Scaredy Cat stared and stared. Then he suddenly heard a low deep voice speaking. 'Good morning, Scaredy Cat!' it said. 'Haven't you ever seen an angel wink before?'

'N-no,' miaowed Scaredy Cat, not even thinking to ask how the angel could understand him. 'Who are you?'

'Oh, I'm just a stone angel. I haven't got a real name. But

I know you, Scaredy Cat; I have watched you coming into church for the last few weeks and I can understand what you say. Do you enjoy the services?'

'Oh, yes,' said Scaredy Cat, still rather amazed, 'but I can't understand everything.'

'Don't worry,' said the Stone Angel, 'I'll help you to understand and explain everything to you.'

'Well,' said Scaredy Cat, beginning to feel a little more confident, 'can you tell me what a church really is, and what happens here?'

'Of course,' said the Stone Angel. 'This is a building where people come each Sunday for the services. A service is a really special time set apart for worshipping God our Heavenly Father, and in praying and listening to the Bible being read. We also sing songs about our Heavenly Father, to show him that we love him. I'll explain some of the other things to you later on.'

'This Heavenly Father sounds like a wonderful person,' said Scaredy Cat. 'I think I'd like to know more about him. If I listen more carefully then perhaps I will.'

'Most certainly you will.' said the Stone Angel.

And from that day on Scaredy Cat went into the church to talk to his friend the Stone Angel, who taught him a great deal, and showed him how he should behave, and what the stories in the Bible really meant.

Scaredy Cat sighed. 'Now,' he thought, 'I have a friend.'

Think about . . .

Do you remember when you first started school, or when you came to Sunday School? What was it like having to make friends with people?

Pray about . . .

Dear God,
　　making friends is difficult;
　　you have to do so much.

You have to listen to them,
　　and get to know them,
　　and learn about them.

But friends are great!

What must it be like
　　to have no friends at all?
I don't think I'd like that.

God,
　　I pray for all those
　　who don't have many friends,
　　or who have difficulty
　　in finding them.

Be a friend to them, God.

Amen.

LOST

Scaredy Cat learns who Jesus is.

Scaredy Cat lapped up the remains of his breakfast, and looked around him. The morning seemed very quiet, and hardly any sounds reached his ears. There was no one about, except for a few birds and a couple of snails on the edge of the lawn. He wondered where everybody had gone.

Taking a leisurely stroll down the garden path, he sniffed at some of the plants which he had dug up yesterday, and pushed his way under some low-lying bushes where it was still very dark. He sat in the middle of the cat-mint for a few minutes, and chewed a long stem of grass missed by the mower.

There was still no one about, and Scaredy Cat yawned. To tell the truth, he was rather bored. He thought of going into the church to talk to his friend the Stone Angel, but he knew that the ladies would be cleaning in there today, and they didn't like him wandering in.

Unusually for him, Scaredy Cat took a giant leap onto the top of the garden wall, to see if he could see any signs of Ginger Tom, but he could neither see nor hear anything.

Next door's garden always seemed to look better than his own. He knew Mr Brown did not have much time for gardening, but the man next door did. Scaredy Cat looked at the neatly mown lawn, the bright patches of flowers stretching into the sun, the bushes with their huge variety of green leaves, and several very tall trees. He jumped down off the wall into the garden and began to search.

However, life was still boring. He could find no trace of the cat next door, or any other sign of life, so he wandered round the garden for a while, and then, with another gigantic leap over a fence, he found himself in the next garden.

He had never been in this garden before, and it was all very new and exciting. They had a pool for one thing, and Scaredy Cat sat beside it wondering if he could play with any of the fish he saw swimming around. After a time, he prowled round the garden inspecting everything in it. Just as he'd had enough of this he saw a gate standing open, so, being a curious cat, he went through it.

To his surprise he found himself standing on the pavement of a road, with other houses nearby, and cars parked alongside. People were walking along and a couple of lorries and cars trundled past him. This was somewhere else he had never been before, and he felt a little unsure of where he ought to go. Seeing another cat on the other side of the road he ran across to say hello, and narrowly missed being run over by a car.

Trotting along, he turned another corner into another road, which looked much the same as before, but there were a few shops at the far end which looked worth investigating.

He sat down outside a baker's shop. The sight of all that food in the window fascinated him – many kinds of loaves, and the most delicious looking cakes and pastries. And to make it worse, the smell of the baking made his mouth water, making him feel very hungry. 'It must be nearly dinner time,' he thought. So he turned round to walk back home.

Then he panicked! Was he going in the right direction? There were so many people, cars raced past him, vans hooted and motor bikes roared along, frightening him. He couldn't remember the way back. Had he crossed the road or not, and which road was it anyway? Suddenly he felt lost and alone and unwanted, and he didn't know what to do. Scaredy Cat sat down on the edge of the pavement and did what he knew best. He miaowed and miaowed and miaowed!

'Scaredy Cat, what on earth are you doing here?' said a familiar voice. Looking up, Scaredy Cat saw a face he recognised peering at him; it was Susan, one of Mr Brown's children who he knew very well. Scaredy Cat tried to tell Susan that he was lost and didn't know the way home, but of course, to her ears, all he said was 'miaow'. Then kind hands picked him up. 'You're lost', said Susan, as though she could read his thoughts. 'I'd better take you back home.'

Scaredy Cat purred a big thank you. Now he felt safe and comfortable again, and he knew that all was going to be well again.

When Mr Brown saw him, he was very surprised. 'Where on earth did you get to?' he asked. 'We were very worried about you.'

'I was worried about me too!' miaowed Scaredy Cat.

Later that day, Scaredy Cat wandered into the church to talk to his friend the Stone Angel. He told him all about his adventures and how he had been frightened when he was lost.

'Your story almost sounds like the story of the lost sheep, which Jesus told,' said the Stone Angel. 'One day a man was looking after a flock of sheep, one hundred of them all together. Then, when he brought them into the sheepfold at night, he counted them and found that one of them had wandered off and was lost. After he secured the other sheep, he set off and searched and searched until he had found it, and returned it to the other sheep.'

'Was he frightened, like me?' asked Scaredy Cat.

'When he found that he was lost, later on, then I think he may have become frightened, because he didn't know how to get home, just like you.'

'I know that when we are frightened, we must remember that God our Father is always near us to help us, just as he did to me,' said Scaredy Cat, 'but who was Jesus who told the story?'

'Jesus,' said the Stone Angel, 'is the only Son of God, our Heavenly Father. He was born just like any other tiny baby and we remember his birthday on a special day called Christmas Day. He grew up to be a young man, and he went around telling others about God our Heavenly Father. He often did this by telling some wonderful stories like the one I have just told you, and also by healing people who were ill.'

'Oh,' said Scaredy Cat, wanting to hear more, 'then I would like to know more about him and his stories.'

'You will,' said the Stone Angel. 'You will.'

Think about . . .

Have you ever felt lost? What did you think when you felt like this? How did you feel when you were found? If you can't think of a time when you have felt like this, try to imagine how Scaredy Cat must have felt.

Pray about . . .

Dear God,
   it's not nice being lost.

You feel alone,
   and helpless.
You don't know what to do.

I've felt like that, God.
But most people do, sometimes.

You don't know where to go
   or what to do.

But, God,
   when we do feel lost,
    you're still there, aren't you?
Thank you, God.

Amen.

OVER THE ROOF

Scaredy Cat learns of God's wonderful creation and the importance of prayer.

Scaredy Cat had been thinking all day, and finally he made up his mind; he would spend the night wandering about to see the night life. He wouldn't go straight to bed and curl up in his box, but spend the whole night exploring. 'In fact,' he thought, 'I think I'll go climbing, and go onto the rooftops of the houses. I haven't had a good climb for ages.'

That night he set off. He walked as far as the fence between the houses and then climbed up onto it. Scrambling along until he reached the end nearest the vicarage, he then jumped onto a low sloping roof at the back of the house. From there he scrambled up a drainpipe until he reached the guttering at the foot of the main roof. A short stiff climb uphill brought him to where he wanted to go, nearly to the very top of the roof. Settling himself down by the chimney pot he watched the world below him.

It was dark of course, but he could still see very clearly, as all cats can. He watched the lights from the houses below him, and those far away too. He looked up and saw the moon and stars twinkling in the dark sky, and listened to the sound of cars and lorries racing past him, unaware that they were being watched. He could see people walking around, going home or taking their dog for a walk. But eventually, and very slowly, the world began to go to bed, and all became quiet and still. This was the time he loved best, as he would soon see his other friends that nobody else knew about.

As he stirred from his position, he disturbed a nest of birds perched near the guttering. He hadn't meant to wake them up, but mother bird settled her chicks down under her wings and they were soon asleep again. He heard the distant sound of an owl hooting far away, and the occasional bark of a dog. After a while, he slowly climbed down again towards the guttering of the roof, and from there he jumped onto the lower roof of the garage. Now he could watch the comings and goings of the garden. He spotted a couple of field mice rushing about looking for food. He was tempted to go and play with them, but he decided against it.

Watching carefully he caught sight of something unexpected, the movement of a fox! Occasionally foxes came into the garden also in search of food. They could see better than he could in the dark, and Scaredy Cat watched fascinated. He saw the fox run from tree to tree and bush to bush, its nose close to the ground. He saw him suddenly stiffen as he spotted the mice, and then crawl slowly towards them, thinking of his supper. The mice saw him, however, and soon ran to a hole in the ground. As the mice disappeared the fox ran off, still hungry.

Scaredy Cat climbed the fence once more, up the drainpipe, and back onto the roof. He then decided to go further afield, so he jumped the narrow gap between the houses and landed quietly onto the next door's roof.

From here he could see more of the road. He watched another dog wandering down the footpath, and then another cat wandering in the opposite direction. Scaredy Cat watched carefully; Ginger Tom was also out on the prowl that night! He climbed to the top of the roof near the chimney pots and the television aerial, and then sat down again. He watched some of the other birds and animals still on the move. The night seemed to be a busy one!

Then Scaredy Cat began to slither down the slope of the roof, still keeping close to the cables of the television aerial, but suddenly he got his feet caught in the cable. Scaredy Cat didn't quite know how it had happened, because he was really a very careful and nimble climber, but somehow his paw seemed to be jammed under the cable which was laid very firmly onto the roofing tiles.

He wriggled his paw this way and that, trying to loosen the grip, when suddenly it came free. The suddenness of the move knocked him off his balance, and he felt himself falling down the roof, until he landed with a thump onto the lower guttering of the house. He looked all around him, and decided to walk along the gutter until he could find a drainpipe to climb down.

He searched for a short while and then found what he had been looking for. He was just about to begin his climb down when he slipped again, and before he knew what was happening he found that he had got both his front paws jammed into the top of the drainpipe. This time he was well and truly stuck.

Scaredy Cat tried several times, but he couldn't free himself. The more he tried the worse his position seemed to get. Eventually he decided to stop trying and stay where he was. Perhaps someone would come and rescue him in the morning.

It was a long and dark night, and the wind was very cold. Scaredy Cat wished, as he shivered, that he had stayed at home. He began to sing to himself, to cheer himself up, but the local birds did not seem to appreciate his musical talents. Then he remembered his chats with his friend the Stone Angel, so he began to pray, and talk to his Heavenly Father. He told God of his problem at that moment, and also how much he loved him, and thanked God for caring for him. He also promised to try and behave himself a bit more. Somehow, in the stillness of the night, Scaredy Cat felt God very near to him, and remembered that God had promised to be with him always.

Eventually the long night began to grow lighter and Scaredy Cat realised that soon it would be day. He heard more sounds of the traffic and people and birds and dogs. He began to miaow loudly, trying to get noticed by someone passing by.

After a short time a window opened, and Scaredy Cat saw a head pushed out and staring up at him. 'Mom, there's a cat stuck in the drainpipe,' it yelled loudly.

After some time and a lot of coming and going by various people, a man put up a ladder close to the drainpipe and slowly climbed to Scaredy Cat. 'How did you get stuck in there?' he asked. Or perhaps I can guess! You're Scaredy Cat, from the vicarage, up to your tricks again!'

'As if I would do such a thing,' thought Scaredy Cat. 'Accidents just seem to happen to me.'

Much later that day, Scaredy Cat trotted round to the church to talk to the Stone Angel. He told him all about the wonderful things he had seen, the moon and stars, the birds and all the other animals, like the mice and the fox.

'It's almost like another world at night,' said the Stone Angel. 'I often hear some very strange sounds. It's all part of God's wonderful world. Because many of us go to sleep at night, we are only aware of what goes on during the daytime, but at night many creatures are up and about. They are all part of God's creation.'

'I'm glad you spent your time talking to our Heavenly Father. Remember he never sleeps, and always listens to us. When you can't sleep it's always a good idea to spend the time praying. Some people spend all night praying, occasionally!'

'I wonder how they manage to keep their eyes open,' yawned Scaredy Cat, before quietly closing his eyes and drifting off to sleep to dream about his night time adventure.

Think about . . .

Do you ever look out of your window at night? Sometimes
the sky is full of stars, and other times it may be really dark
and stormy. Sometimes you may even see the setting sun!

Pray about . . .

Dear God,
I love your world!
I think it's wonderful!

There is so much to see
    and so much to do.
Will I have time?
I hope so.

There are so many animals,
    and plants.
And then there's the weather!
I love it when it's sunny, God!
Even thunderstorms can be fun!
(As long as I'm hiding under my duvet!)

This world is a great place, God.
I am glad I live here.

Help us all to look after it.

Amen.

SPLASH

Scaredy Cat learns what it means to be a Christian.

Once again, Scaredy Cat was bored. For the last two days it had poured with rain and he had only occasionally gone outside, but had soon had to hurry back into the house. He had played at chasing the mice in the church, but they did not seem keen to play with him. He had spent a lot of time sleeping, but now he was no longer tired. There just didn't seem to be anything around to play with; no knitting wool, no pieces of fluff, no crumbs left on the kitchen floor. Not a thing! He even tried watching the television when it was turned on, but he couldn't understand most of it. He was just plain bored.

Then, on the third day, after he had nibbled at his breakfast, he suddenly realised that it had stopped raining. It was still cold and there was no sign of the sun, but he could at least go outside and play in the garden.

The night before it had been very stormy, and Scaredy Cat saw that part of the fence between his garden and the one next door had been blown down during the night, so he trotted through the gap in the fence to look round the garden next door.

The wind was blowing, leaves were swirling around, and he spent some time trying to catch them in his paws. He noticed that there was no one around at all. He began to run across the lawn just for some exercise, when he stopped suddenly. There in front of him was a pool, a real pool, with plants growing in it, fish swimming around, and many more creatures that Scaredy Cat had never seen before.

Slowly he crept forwards and stood at the edge of the pool. Deep in the water he could see all kinds of shapes of fish, some only tiny and some quite large ones. He watched them twist and turn and dive and come up again for air or for tiny bits of food. He was fascinated by their colours: silver, silvery-blue, red, brown and a few shiny orange ones which Scaredy Cat knew were goldfish. Scaredy Cat watched them playing and enjoying themselves in the water, and he began to feel hungry. After all he did love to eat fish, and he thought that they would make a lovely dinner instead of his usual food!

As he watched he saw one quite large fish with a silver body but red fins lazily swim ever nearer and nearer to him. As he watched Scaredy Cat began to wonder if he could just reach in and flip it out.

Slowly and carefully he stretched out his paw, keeping close to the shadows where he could not be seen so clearly. Then with a sudden quick movement he plunged his paw into the cold water to flip out the large fish. Unfortunately for Scaredy Cat, he missed, as the fish suddenly dived down deeply. Scaredy Cat sat perched on the very edge of the pool feeling very disappointed, and as he gazed into the water, watching the escaping fish, he lost his balance. Clutching wildly at the air, he fell head-over-heels into the icy water.

The water was very cold indeed, and Scaredy Cat did not like water very much. He spluttered and splashed about, and miaowed for help. At first he thought that he might have to stay there in the cold water, but soon he heard voices, so he continued to miaow as loudly as he could for help; 'MIAOW, MIAOW, MIAOW!'

As the voices came nearer, Scaredy Cat was able to see that they were the children from the vicarage, and some of the children from the house next door also. 'Oh, poor Scaredy Cat, he must have fallen into the pond!' cried Susan.

'More likely he was after the fish!' said David.

'Well,' thought Scaredy Cat, 'as if I would!'

Quickly several hands reached out to him, and slowly a dripping wet, soggy moggy was lifted onto the bank by the pool. He felt cold and frightened and miserable.

The children picked him up once more, getting very wet themselves in the process, and rushed into the house with him. They found an old towel, and began to gently dry Scaredy Cat who was beginning to enjoy all the attention and hugs from the children. Finally he was placed near a warm fire with a saucerful of milk. Eventually he began to feel a little better, and miaowed his thanks to the children. He didn't seem to have hurt himself and he felt much more comfortable than sitting in the fish pond.

Before long the children carried him, still wrapped in the towel, back to the vicarage and explained what had happened. It had been quite an adventurous day after all. Mr Brown would not let him go out again that day but made him stay by the fire until he was quite dry and well after his shock.

The next day Scaredy Cat lost no time in going round to the church to talk to his friend the Stone Angel, and share his experiences with him.

'I nearly drowned!' declared Scaredy Cat rather proudly.

'Yes indeed,' said the Stone Angel. 'I hope that you thanked the children properly. They have been very kind to you, and a Christian should always learn to say thank you for every kindness shown to him. Jesus healed ten men who were very ill, and they all felt better again. Only one of them, however, turned back to thank him!'

'Oh yes,' said Scaredy Cat, 'I remember the story for it was read in church one day. I am certain, too, that when I was in the water, my Heavenly Father heard my cries for help, and he sent the children to rescue me.'

'Just so,' said the Stone Angel.

Now that Scaredy Cat was feeling better, he had a question to ask the Stone Angel. 'What is a Christian?' he purred.

'Oh,' said the Stone Angel, 'a Christian is a person who has learned to love our Heavenly Father. He trusts in him, and tries to do the things God wants him to do. I think that you have learned to love him too.'

'Oh yes,' cried Scaredy Cat, 'I do.'

Think about . . .

What do you think it means to be a Christian?

Pray about . . .

Dear God,
    being a Christian isn't easy.
There is so much to think about.
So much to do.

Like having to be nice to everybody,
    even if we don't like them.
That really isn't easy at all, God.
Especially if someone annoys you.

But there's more to it than that.
We need to help each other,
    and love each other.

We need to work together
    and love you, God.

Help us to do that, God.

Amen.

TAIL GATE

Scaredy Cat learns his first lesson on being kind.

'Yarroo! MMMIIAAOOWW! Miaow! Miaow!' The Stone Angel in the church stirred as he heard an unmistakable voice yelling and howling and screaming as loud as could be. Slowly the voice trailed away as it carried round the church and into the direction of the vicarage. 'Oh, dear,' thought the Stone Angel, 'now what has Scaredy Cat been up to?'

True, Scaredy Cat was in trouble again, but it wasn't exactly his fault this time. Yesterday he had watched a man fitting a new catch onto the little gate which was across the path from the vicarage to the church itself. Then the hinges on the gate had broken, so the man had been forced to replace them with much larger and stronger ones, and Scaredy Cat noticed that the gate now shut behind you more quickly, and in a rather fierce way.

Forgetting this, the next day Scaredy Cat trotted down the path towards the church to talk to his old friend the Stone Angel. He trotted to the gate, pushed it open with his head, and trotted through it. Unfortunately, he was not quick enough! The gate shut behind him with a loud clang and poor Scaredy Cat was caught in it. He managed to run through quickly enough, but, his tail caught in the gate, and it pinched his tail so hard that it looked almost bent! Poor Scaredy Cat hopped around yelling and howling in cat fashion, and then ran into the vicarage again by another route in order to seek some comfort from the family.

The pain was awful, and poor Scaredy Cat hardly knew what to do to ease his discomfort. Very slowly the aching and pain died down, but when Scaredy Cat inspected his tail later on, it seemed to him to have a definite bend in it, and it remained sore for many days afterwards.

It wasn't just the pain which hurt Scaredy Cat so much, but the indignity of it all. It had happened during the school holidays, and a number of children were outside, passing the church. When they saw what had happened, they just burst out laughing at him, and thought the whole thing was very funny. Scaredy Cat couldn't see anything funny in it at all!

Later on, Scaredy Cat limped into the church to talk to his friend once more. The Stone Angel asked him what had happened, and Scaredy Cat told him all the details. 'I suppose it was my own fault really,' he said, 'but I simply forgot about the new hinges on the gate, and it gave me a terrible fright when the gate shut tight on me!'

'What was even worse,' said the Stone Angel, 'was that those children did not help you, but only laughed at your unfortunate accident. They could have helped you.'

'Yes,' said Scaredy Cat. 'Isn't there a verse in the Bible which says that we must be kind to each other? I'm sure I heard it being read in Church last week.'

'Yes,' said the Stone Angel. 'It says be kind and compassionate to one another, forgiving each other.'

'I remember,' said Scaredy Cat. 'I also remember Mr Brown saying that we should be kind to all people, no matter who they are; and that we should also be kind to animals and birds and fish too!'

'That's right, and thousands of years ago, we were told to treat animals well, and not to overwork them,' replied the Stone Angel.

'Well I wish they would remember that nowadays,' retorted Scaredy Cat, as he turned, said goodbye to the Stone Angel and wandered from the church.

As he strolled outside, he felt like a rest so decided to sit down and watch the birds in the churchyard flying around and coming down to peck at tiny bits of food or insects. He sometimes wished that he could fly. What would it be like up in the sky, to fly around and see all the houses and gardens from a great height?

Suddenly he froze. He just caught a glimpse of Ginger Tom from next door. He was hiding from somebody, thought Scaredy Cat. Then Scaredy Cat suddenly realised that Ginger Tom was watching the birds himself. He was going to try and catch one!

Now Scaredy Cat liked to chase the birds himself, but he knew that they would never let him catch them, and he knew that they were much too fast for him. He never caught one, and even if he did, he would let it go anyway. Then Scaredy Cat remembered what he had been saying to the Stone Angel a few minutes before. 'We must be kind, not only to other animals, but also to the birds and fish as well.' What if Ginger Tom caught one of the birds?

Scaredy Cat watched Ginger Tom, as he slowly crept towards a group of birds feeding on the ground, and slowly flattened himself, ready to spring on them. Without a thought Scaredy Cat leaped into action. He jumped to his feet and fairly flew at Ginger Tom. The birds saw him coming and flew away. They were out of danger now, but Ginger Tom was not very pleased.

Ginger Tom scowled at Scaredy Cat. 'You've ruined my day,' he said. 'Those birds will never come near me again!' He then chased Scaredy Cat back into the vicarage, eventually sitting down to dream of how he could get his own back on Scaredy Cat. He was not happy that he would have to wait until supper time for his food.

Think about . . .

How do you feel if someone is kind to you, especially when you aren't expecting it? How do you think someone else feels if you are kind to them?

Pray about . . .

Dear God,
  I like it when people
  are kind to me.

When they help me,
  or give me something,
  or encourage me.

It makes me feel
  that they care.

And, God,
  I like being kind
  to others.

Not so that it makes me
  feel good,
  but because I know
  how it feels
  when someone is kind to you.

God,
  help us all to be kind
  to one another.

Maybe then,
  we will be
  a little more
  like you.

  Amen.

VANISHING TRICK

Scaredy Cat learns the meaning of forgiveness.

'Bang, bang, bang!' Scaredy Cat woke up with a start. He had been sleeping peacefully all afternoon in the kitchen of the old vicarage, when someone had knocked hard on the front door. Needless to say, Scaredy Cat did not miss an opportunity to find out who it was.

Much to his surprise, when Mr Brown opened the door, Scaredy Cat saw two men with a very heavy, odd-looking parcel, which they brought into the Vicarage, and carried into the main living room.

Mr Brown looked very pleased, and when he had cut away all the paper and card wrapping, Scaredy Cat saw that it was a brand-new chair, in a lovely shiny red-brown wood, with comfortable-looking cushions on it.

Mr Brown sat on it and tried it out, and then called to his wife to try it out too. 'There,' he said to her, 'your present has arrived at last. Isn't it beautiful?' They both seemed very pleased with it, and Scaredy Cat thought that it looked very handsome.

During the evening, Mrs Brown sat in her new armchair doing her knitting, while Mr Brown was writing some letters. Then she left her knitting on her chair and went to make a cup of tea before they went to bed that night.

During the night, Scaredy Cat woke up and gazed sleepily from his bed in the kitchen. He was not sure what had made him wake up, but he decided to have a walk round the rooms to stretch his legs. He wandered into the living room to look at the new armchair, and to his excitement, he saw that Mr Brown's wife had left her knitting on the seat of the chair, and a ball of wool had rolled on the floor.

Now Scaredy Cat loved to play with wool, and he immediately pounced on the wool and began to play with it, using it like a football, and rolling it all over the floor.

At one point it seemed to get stuck, so Scaredy Cat climbed onto the seat to pull down the rest of the wool. After a while, however, he grew tired and so went back to sleep on his bed in the kitchen.

'Scaredy Cat!' screamed a voice from somewhere in the house, waking Scaredy Cat with a start. It was Mr Brown, calling his name rather angrily from the living room. He crept into the room, and stood there gazing at the mess he had made of the ball of wool pulled from the knitting. But Mr Brown was not looking at this at all, but at the new armchair.

Scaredy Cat shivered when he saw what he had done, for there, down one leg of the chair was a long, deep scratch, undoubtedly caused by his claws. Scaredy Cat was in trouble again.

After Mr Brown had shouted at him again, Scaredy Cat crept under the table in the kitchen, and kept well out of the way for most of the day. He heard people coming and going but he did not bother to go and find out who it was. He heard someone in the living room and he was there for some time, but he still did not go in.

That evening, Mr Brown and his wife went out to a meeting in the church, and Scaredy Cat was left to his own devices, but curiosity got the better of him, and he wandered once more into the living room to look at the scratch on the armchair.

When he went into the room, Scaredy Cat noticed a strange smell he had not come across before. He couldn't think what it could be, and it certainly didn't smell like any food that he had ever had. It seemed to come from the new armchair, and when Scaredy Cat went to investigate this, he suddenly stood stock still, unable to believe his eyes. He carefully looked at the leg of the chair he had scratched, but the scratch had vanished! It was no longer there, and the strange smell seemed to come from the leg. Scaredy Cat slowly walked round the chair, inspecting all the other legs, to make sure that he had not made a mistake, but there was no sign of the scratch. What had happened to it? Where had it gone?

He wandered back into the kitchen, and lay down again trying to puzzle out what had been going on. Perhaps it was some kind of mysterious trick, he thought. And what was that puzzling strange smell? He decided to consult his friend, the Stone Angel, the next day.

The next day the Stone Angel listened quietly as Scaredy Cat poured out his tale of mystery and woe that he had experienced. Suddenly Scaredy Cat was surprised to hear the Stone Angel chuckling. 'I know all about your problems,' said the Stone Angel, 'because there was a meeting here in the church last night, and I heard Mr Brown telling some of the people all about it. I also know what happened to your disappearing scratch,' he added.

'Yesterday,' he continued, 'Mr Brown called in a man

who is a french polisher and he smoothed out the scratch, stained it over, and repolished the chair leg. That was the funny smell and that was how the scratch disappeared.'

'Oh,' said Scaredy Cat, 'now I understand. It made it look as though nothing had ever happened.'

'Just so,' said the Stone Angel, 'and that is exactly how forgiveness works. When we do anything wrong, then God our Heavenly Father forgives us if we ask him and say we are sorry. So God wipes the wrong thing away, and it cannot be found any more. He says that the things we do wrong he will remember no more. They just do not exist any more.'

'How wonderful!' said Scaredy Cat. 'So that is what forgiveness is all about!'

Think about . . .

How do you feel when you've done something wrong?
What is it like if someone does something that upsets you?
What is it that makes things like this better?

Pray about . . .

Dear God,
   I don't like it
   when I get into trouble.
I upset people,
   and everything feels horrible.
I even cry, sometimes.

And, God,
   it's not nice
   when people upset me,
   because I can get angry.

But when things
   have calmed down,
   and we forgive each other
   it is better.
Everything is forgotten.

You taught us this, God.
Thank you.

Amen.

THE FIGHT

Scaredy Cat learns his second lesson in being kind.

Scaredy Cat came limping into the church one morning. The Stone Angel stared at him. 'Whatever has happened to you?' he asked. 'You look a mess.'

'I've been in a fight!' said Scaredy Cat, smugly.

'I can see that,' said the Stone Angel, 'Just look at you! Your fur has been pulled out in great patches, your tail looks as though it's been run over, your ears are hanging half off, and you look as though you've got a black eye!'

'I've been fighting Ginger Tom from next door,' said Scaredy Cat. 'And I won!' he added rather proudly.

The Stone Angel stared at him again. 'Fighting?' he said, 'what did you fight about?'

'Well,' said Scaredy Cat, 'he came into my garden, sat down on my favourite spot, and then he sneaked up and stole some of my breakfast. So we had a fight. He's got to learn who's boss around here, and he'll never do it again. So I reckon that I won.'

'No, you didn't,' interrupted the Stone Angel, 'you lost.'

'Oh no,' said Scaredy Cat. 'I won. He'll never do it again.'

'Very likely,' said the Stone Angel, 'but you still lost.'

'How's that?' asked Scaredy Cat.

'You lost because you forgot some very important things,' replied the Stone Angel. 'To start with, you forgot that Jesus said that you must learn to love your enemies, not fight them. For another thing, you forgot that you should never lose your temper with Ginger Tom or anybody else. And finally, you seem to forget that if you hate somebody, it will be like a shadow over your life, a shadow that will grow darker and darker each day.'

'Oh!' whispered Scaredy Cat. 'It must be very hard to love your enemy; in fact it seems almost impossible!'

'Hard, yes, but not impossible,' said the Stone Angel. 'If you ask Jesus, he will help you. His love will shine through you, and you will learn to love even the people you didn't like.'

'How do I do that?' asked Scaredy Cat.

'Well this is what we call prayer. When all the people come to church you see them bow their heads and close their eyes. They are praying. When we do that we can talk to God our Heavenly Father and to Jesus his Son. He will always listen to us when we talk to him, and if we ask him to help us, he usually will.'

'Well, what should I do now?' asked Scaredy Cat.

'Try talking to Ginger Tom, and being friends with him,' replied the Stone Angel. 'See if you can help him, and be prepared to share things with him.'

'*Friends*!' retorted Scaredy Cat in disbelief. 'He has no friends because no one likes him.'

'Precisely! Now is your chance to show him that you really want to care for him,' said the Stone Angel.

Scaredy Cat slowly crept out of the church, thinking about all that the Stone Angel had said to him. 'I wonder why it's so hard to be good?' he said to himself. 'The Stone Angel asks me to do some very hard things, and I'm sure that they will never work.' As he walked out of the church doorway, he turned a corner and came face to face with Ginger Tom. In spite of himself, Scaredy Cat's fur stood on end, and he bared his teeth.

'Hello,' said Ginger Tom grinning, 'how are you?'

'Not too bad,' said Scaredy Cat, 'how are you?'

'Could be better,' grunted Ginger Tom, 'do you feel like another fight, or shall we wait till tomorrow?'

Scaredy Cat took a deep breath. 'I've been thinking,' he said slowly. 'Your garden is full of big trees, so there probably isn't much sunshine in it. It must be all dark and cold.'

'It's freezing in there most of the time,' admitted Ginger Tom suspiciously. 'Why?'

'Well, when the sun shines, my garden is lovely and warm, and there are some beautiful spots for going to sleep in. Why not come into my garden some time, instead, and have a nice snooze there?'

Ginger Tom eyed Scaredy Cat warily. 'Well,' he said slowly, 'that's very kind of you, thank you. To be perfectly honest, I'm not a greedy cat, and I've usually got plenty of food, I suppose. If you get hungry sometimes, feel free to have a nibble at my breakfast.'

Suddenly the two cats began to talk together. They ambled down the path to Scaredy Cat's favourite spot. With some shuffling, they both lay down together, and soon they dozed off. Just before they fell asleep, Ginger Tom said 'I'm sorry for what I did.'

'And so am I,' replied Scaredy Cat.

Soon the air was filled with the sound of their snoring. Inside the church the Stone Angel watched them through the window, and he smiled quietly to himself. He knew that it would take a long time for Scaredy Cat and Ginger Tom to become close friends, but he could see that a start had been made.

Think about . . .

Admitting that you're wrong can be difficult sometimes. Why do you think this is?

Pray about . . .

Dear God,
   being wrong isn't nice,
   especially if you thought
   you were right,
   only to discover
   you weren't.

You have to own up,
   say sorry,
   and hope for forgiveness.

And when you do,
   you can be friends again.

Just like Scaredy Cat
   and Ginger Tom.

Help me be like this
   more and more, God.

Amen.

CLUMSY CAT

Scaredy Cat learns how to say he is sorry.

There was only one room in the vicarage that Scaredy Cat very rarely entered: Mr Brown's study. It wasn't that he was not allowed into the study, but that the study never seemed to be very interesting to an enterprising cat like himself. Mr Brown, he knew, spent a lot of time in the place, and often talked to other people in there; but he also insisted on keeping it very tidy and wouldn't allow any mess of any sort in the room. A tidy room was not Scaredy Cat's idea of an interesting room and he saw little reason for exploring it.

One day, however, when everybody else was out in the garden enjoying some sunshine and some gardening, Scaredy Cat noticed that the study door, which was both large and heavy, had been left open in order to air the place. Scaredy Cat, with nothing else to do at the time, decided to go and have a look around this rather boring room. There was a nice red carpet on the floor which was quite soft to Scaredy Cat's paws, and the whole room seemed full of books. There were bookcases covering nearly all the walls, tables with books on them, a filing cabinet with a stack of books sitting on the top, a couple of chairs piled high with more books, and, by the window stood Mr Brown's desk. The desk was also covered with books, and papers of all sorts, a telephone, and also a vase of flowers. The whole place seemed to have a very musty, dusty smell to it.

Scaredy Cat could see very little of interest to him. After all, he couldn't read the books, and he probably wouldn't have understood them if he could. He jumped upon the chair, and with a stretch climbed upon Mr Brown's desk. He prowled round looking at all the papers on the desk, some of which were written with Mr Brown's own neat handwriting. Probably his sermon for Sunday, thought Scaredy Cat.

Suddenly the telephone began to ring, and Scaredy Cat jumped with fright, even though he had heard it many times before. This time, however, no one came to answer it; they had probably been unable to hear it in the garden. The telephone attracted Scaredy Cat's attention. He had never been so close to one before, and he wondered how it worked. What made it ring, and how could you hear people speaking into it? He brushed against the instrument, knocking it slightly, and the receiver suddenly seemed to jump up as Scaredy Cat got his feet tangled with the wire. The sudden movement of the telephone receiver made Scaredy Cat jump himself and he turned round suddenly, brushing against the vase of flowers. Two seconds later, the vase came crashing down on the desk, breaking the glass, and spilling water all over the top of the desk.

Scaredy Cat stared in dismay at the mess. For one thing he had to tread carefully so that he did not cut his paws on the broken glass, but in doing this he put his feet all in the water, which seemed to spread everywhere, and make all the papers swim in it. Somehow the papers began to attach themselves to his feet, so that walking was more difficult, and the water seemed to drip over the edge of the desk and onto the carpet. Scaredy Cat stared at the terrible mess he had made and was rather pleased with himself. He hadn't made this much mess since he was a tiny kitten!

Then he heard the heavy tread of Mr Brown coming back inside the house. When he came into his study he seemed to explode with anger, and shook his fist at Scaredy Cat. 'Trust you to find your way in here,' he yelled, 'and now just look at the mess you have made! All my letters are ruined, and all my sermon notes are unreadable now. I shall have to do all this work again. You are a very naughty cat!' he thundered. 'When will you learn? You can just do without your supper tonight. Perhaps that will teach you a lesson.'

With that he picked Scaredy Cat off his desk and took him into the kitchen to his usual place. Then he got a pan, brushed up all the broken glass, and put it into the dust-bin. Then he had to start and clean up the soggy paper and water on his desk.

'Oh dear,' thought Scaredy Cat. 'Here we go again. Will I ever be out of trouble?' Mr Brown came back into the kitchen for a cloth to clear away all the water. He continued to shout at Scaredy Cat for some time, and then he called for someone else to come and help him. Scaredy Cat stayed well out of the way for the rest of that unfortunate day.

The following afternoon, as usual, he wandered into the church to report the day's events to the Stone Angel. 'I didn't mean to do it,' he wailed, 'but the telephone receiver coming off the telephone made me jump with surprise, and rather frightened me. It made such an awful mess. What should I do about it?'

The Stone Angel chuckled to himself as he thought of the mess that one tiny cat had made. Scaredy Cat was certainly good at getting into trouble. However, he kept his face straight and looked gravely at the little cat. 'You have certainly been very naughty,' he said. 'If you had kept off the desk as you have been told to do before, than that accident would never have happened.'

'I know,' sighed Scaredy Cat, 'but it was a pure accident. What can I do about it now?'

'Well,' said the Stone Angel, 'first of all you must learn to say that you are sorry. People will be more likely to forgive you, if you say sorry.'

'I know that,' said Scaredy Cat, 'but how can I do that when nobody knows what I am saying?'

'That is a problem,' replied the Stone Angel. 'Perhaps you could show them how sorry you are. Can you think of something you could do to show them that you are really sorry, and that you meant no harm?'

Scaredy Cat thought for a long time. 'Well,' he said slowly, 'I could earn my keep I suppose. Do you think it would help if I went out and chased a few of the mice that still live in the vicarage?'

'You could certainly try it,' said the Stone Angel with a smile.

Think about . . .

How do you say sorry? What does it feel like? Do you ever think about blaming someone else? What is wrong with doing this?

Pray about . . .

Dear God,
　　saying sorry is never easy.

There are times
　　when I don't want to.
When I'd rather run away,
　　in the hope that what I'd done
　　would not be noticed,
　　or blamed on someone else.

It's because I'm scared.
I don't like seeing people upset.
Especially if it's my fault.

But, God,
　　saying sorry is the only way out.
Admitting I'm wrong
　　makes me feel better
　　and shows that I'm honest.

Help me to be more honest, God.

Amen.

*Scaredy Cat learns that we
cannot cover up our mistakes.*

Scaredy Cat was a very curious cat. He always wanted to know who people were, what they were doing, or what was going on. He loved to sniff around new things that appeared, and watch people who were doing jobs around the house or the church.

One day he saw two men, who arrived at the church with lots of tools and one of those big noisy machines which seemed to make cement. One of the men Scaredy Cat knew to be the churchwarden, and the other man seemed to be helping him.

Mr Brown, arrived and talked to them for a few minutes. They were looking at the path which led from the church gate to the door of the church. Scaredy Cat had noticed that it seemed to be in a poor state, and that the path was breaking into pieces, making it quite hard for cats to walk on. He concluded that they were going to repair it.

'Now, Scaredy Cat,' said Mr Brown firmly to him, 'you mustn't get in the way. Keep right off the path because it will take a long time to dry when it is finished.'

Scaredy Cat felt rather disappointed but he did continue to watch from a distance. All that morning the two men worked hard, breaking up the old path and carting it away. Then they started up their noisy machine which seemed to make cement, and slowly they laid it on the old path, filling in the holes and making the surface very smooth. They did a good job, but they took most of the day to finish it.

At the end they put up a kind of little fence of sticks with string round them to stop people walking on it until it was dry, and Scaredy Cat even helped them by chasing off a little bird who nearly landed on it. At last Scaredy

Cat went to get his supper. He had worked hard all day!

The next day, after breakfast, Scaredy Cat decided to go out and inspect the new path. All seemed well, with no marks on it and the little fence still in place. Soon, he thought, they will need to take the fence away again so that people could get into the church. Anyway the new path seemed to be quite dry and firm. He hadn't been able to see his friend the Stone Angel for two days, so he trotted up the path and through the door to have a chat with him.

He had just finished telling the Stone Angel all about what the men had been doing with the path when he heard another door open and shut in the church, and Mr Brown came striding towards him. 'Scaredy Cat!' he thundered, 'you are a very naughty cat! Do you realise what you have done?' Scaredy Cat simply didn't understand what he was talking about.

'You,' said Mr Brown, 'have just walked up the path to the church door, and left all those marks on the wet cement.'

'Wet cement?' thought Scaredy Cat, 'what is he talking

51

about? The cement was quite dry when I trod on it.' Out loud he miaowed, 'It wasn't me, it must have been someone else!' But of course Mr Brown couldn't understand him.

'From now on,' said Mr Brown, 'you must stay away from the church until I tell you that you can go back in. Now I shall have to get the men back again to repair the path.'

Scaredy Cat went to the door of the church that he had used, and there, sure enough, was a set of paw prints right along the new path. 'Oh dear,' he thought, 'I'm in trouble again, and to make it worse Mr Brown has told me I can't have my dinner today!' For several days after this, Scaredy Cat kept well away.

That same evening he ate his supper hungrily, but he also kept out of everybody's way, especially the two men who had to come back and do the job again. Most of all he felt miserable because he didn't get into the church to talk to his friend the Stone Angel.

A few days later he saw that the little string fence had been taken down, and people were going into church along the repaired path. It seemed safe once more, to go and see his friend, and so, when all was quiet once more, he crept into the church, and up the aisle to his favourite place near the radiator.

After a few minutes the Stone Angel spoke. 'Ah,' he said, 'I was wondering when you were going to come and see me.'

'I was in trouble,' said Scaredy Cat. 'I thought that the path was dry, but it wasn't, and I left prints all along the path.'

'I know,' said the Stone Angel.

'How did you know that?' asked Scaredy Cat.

'For one thing,' said the Stone Angel, 'cement takes much longer to dry than you think. For another thing, I could see the wet cement on your paws. But you are a very silly cat because you made two mistakes, and forgot something.'

'What did I do wrong?' asked Scaredy Cat innocently.

'Well for one thing you disobeyed Mr Brown, because you thought it didn't matter. Doing as you are told is very important,' said the Stone Angel.

'Where would we all be if we all did what we wanted to do instead of obeying instructions? Look at all the accidents there would be on the road! The other thing, which is even worse, is that you told lies and tried to blame it on someone else. The more lies you tell, the worse the situation becomes. Honesty is very important indeed.'

'Oh, and what did I forget?' asked Scaredy Cat.

'Somehow the things you do wrong have a habit of showing up again. Your wrong things certainly showed up again because your paw prints gave you away,' said the Stone Angel. 'Remember, if we do something wrong, we can ask our Heavenly Father to forgive us, and if we mean it, he will do so.'

'Oh dear,' said Scaredy Cat, 'there seems to be such a lot to remember.'

'Just keep on trying,' said the Stone Angel.

Think about . . .

Imagine that you've broken a piece of your mum's valuable dinner service. What thoughts cross your mind? Should you own up? Do you ever think of trying to hide what you've done?

Pray about . . .

Dear God,
   there are times
   when I've made a mistake
   or done something I didn't mean to,
   that I sometimes think
   if I tried to cover up what I'd done,
   and hide the evidence,
   I could get away with it.

That's not very nice,
   is it, God?

I know I should own up,
   and I do,
   but I still think, 'what if . . .'

Help me, God,
   to own up,
   and not to try and run away
   from what I've done.

Amen.

STUCK

Scaredy Cat learns the real meaning of faith.

Early one morning Scaredy Cat went into the church to talk to his friend the Stone Angel. 'What does it mean to have faith in God?' he asked.

The Stone Angel thought back to what Mr Brown had said in church a day or two before about faith. 'Faith', he said, 'means to trust completely. When we have faith in God it means we must trust him to do what is best for us all the time.'

Scaredy Cat thought about this for a time. 'I have faith that Mrs Brown will feed me every day – I know she wouldn't forget me.'

'It's just like that,' said the Stone Angel. 'We must trust that God our Heavenly Father will never forget us.'

'Now I understand,' said Scaredy Cat and he trotted out of the church.

Scaredy Cat was usually a very friendly sort of cat. He didn't argue or fight with other cats, and he always greeted visitors with a friendly 'Miaow' and rubbed round their feet or allowed them to stroke him. He even purred on occasions, and he never scratched them.

However, there was one thing that Scaredy Cat hated, and that was dogs. Well, perhaps he didn't 'hate' them, because some of them could be friendly. But they were always bigger than he was, and very fierce, and they made a lot of noise. To be perfectly honest, he was really very frightened of them, for they always seemed to want to chase him, and they often ran faster than he could. He had talked to the Stone Angel in the church about this quite often, but that didn't always help. The Stone Angel pointed out that they were all God's creatures, made and loved by Him. But that only seemed to make it worse.

That day Scaredy Cat was dozing in his favourite place in the garden, when he heard a car pull up. The Browns had got some visitors. Then he stiffened, for he heard the sound of a dog barking, loud barks. They went into the house, and Scaredy Cat hoped that they would stay there. Then, a few minutes later, he heard the back door open, and out raced the dog, straight for him. He seemed to take one look at Scaredy Cat, and bounded straight towards him, barking loudly.

Scaredy Cat got up, his hair standing on end, trying to make himself look bigger than he really was, but the dog continued to follow, bounding straight towards him. In sheer panic, Scaredy Cat began to run down the garden, hiding under some bushes, but the dog kept on running. Scaredy Cat raced round and round again, until he came to the big tall tree at the end of the garden.

With claws spread out, he heaved himself up the first two or three feet of the trunk of the tree, but the big dog reached the tree, and then began jumping up at him. So Scaredy Cat struggled further up the tree until he reached the safety of the first branch.

Scaredy Cat turned to watch the dog, and to his horror the dog began to try to climb up the trunk of the tree getting closer and closer to him. Scaredy Cat knew there was only one way he could go, and that was upwards. So he began to climb again, until he scrambled, breathlessly, to the next high branch. As this was a strong branch, Scaredy Cat crept out along it until he almost reached the end. There he stopped, realising that the dog was too heavy to climb after him any more. At last he was safe.

The dog stopped howling and barking and slowly slid back down the tree to the ground. He knew when he was beaten. However, instead of running away, he lay down at the foot of the tree, getting his breath back, and waiting for Scaredy Cat to come down. Scaredy Cat stayed where he was for some time, until he heard a whistle from the back door of the house. This brought the dog to his feet and he ambled back to his owner, who bade farewell to Mr Brown, and they all went away.

Scaredy Cat waited a few minutes, and then decided to gingerly climb down the tree. By now the wind had sprung up and the thin end of the branch that held Scaredy Cat began to sway rather dangerously. Scaredy Cat looked down and saw that he was a long way up. With the swaying of the branch and the long drop down, he began to feel dizzy, and when he tried to turn round he began to feel afraid. Suddenly he realised that he was stuck, and that he couldn't get down again, and he didn't know what to do about it. He might have to stay there for ages, perhaps days or even weeks! Scaredy Cat clung onto his precarious position, and did the only thing he could think of doing, he cried 'MIAOW!', very loudly, over and over again.

After some time Mr Brown came out of the back door with Scaredy Cat's dinner in his dish. He called Scaredy Cat for several minutes, and Scaredy Cat called back again, but Mr Brown could not see where he was until he looked up, and there was Scaredy Cat swinging dangerously from the end of a very high branch of the tree. 'Wait a minute Scaredy Cat!' he called, 'You're stuck! I'll rescue you.'

Scaredy Cat heard him go into the garage, and a few minutes later he pushed his way out of the door, with a very long ladder. Puffing and panting, Mr Brown heaved the very heavy ladder to the end of the garden, and got it set against the tree. Slowly he climbed the ladder until he reached the branch on which Scaredy Cat continued to cling. Slowly he reached out his hands. 'Jump Scaredy Cat!' he called. 'Jump and I'll catch you!' So Scaredy Cat jumped, trustingly, and landed safely in Mr Brown's arms. Slowly they descended the ladder together, and when they reached the ground, Scaredy Cat miaowed his grateful thanks.

Mr Brown stroked him quietly. 'That must have scared you,' he said, 'but you're quite safe now.'

Later that day Scaredy Cat crept into the church to talk to his friend the Stone Angel, and tell him all about his adventures earlier that day.

'You could have easily been killed,' said the Stone Angel, 'but Mr Brown kindly rescued you.'

'I know,' said Scaredy Cat, 'and I thanked him for that. I think that God our Heavenly Father must have heard my crying, and sent him to rescue me.'

'Exactly,' said the Stone Angel, 'and when he called to you to jump, you trusted him, and he helped you. That is just what God often asks us to do. Just trust him, just as we said this morning.'

'I know,' said Scaredy Cat happily, 'and it works.'

Think about . . .

Have you ever seen someone parachuting? What do you think they are thinking as they stand at the door of the plane and look out? How would you feel?

Pray about . . .

Dear God,
  sometimes
  when I'm feeling unsure
  or scared of something
  it's not nice.

It's like walking in the dark
  without a torch.

I can't see where I'm going.

Help me, God,
  to trust you.
To know that you will help me,
  even if I think
  it all looks a bit scary.

Amen.

HELPING ALPHONSE

Scaredy Cat learns how to be a Good Samaritan.

Scaredy Cat sat chatting to the Stone Angel in church one day. As usual he was telling him all the day's events and they were discussing about the meaning of the Bible readings in church the day before.

'Does that mean,' asked Scaredy Cat, 'that the Good Samaritan was good because he helped other people, even though he may not have liked them?'

'It means just that,' said the Stone Angel. 'We must always be on the look-out for ways of helping others, when they are in need, even if we hardly know them, or don't like them.'

'Well, I don't know of anybody I don't really like, and I can't always help others when they won't let me or because I can't do it. It's not a very easy thing to do for a cat,' he declared.

At that moment Scaredy Cat caught a quick movement of something out of the corner of his eye. The Stone Angel had seen it too, and asked what it was.

'I think that's Alphonse,' said Scaredy Cat.

'Who's Alphonse?' asked the Stone Angel.

'Oh, he's the church mouse!' declared Scaredy Cat. 'He lives under the organ in the church. He likes it there usually, except on Sundays when the man comes to play the organ. Then it gets too noisy for him! He's a very quiet mouse, really, and doesn't come outside very often.'

Seeing that they were talking about him, Alphonse crept rather timidly towards the cat. They were old friends really, and Scaredy Cat had given up chasing him a long time ago. 'Oh dear, oh dear, oh dear,' whispered Alphonse in a rather squeaky voice, 'I'm really in very great trouble, I really am, I really am.' Alphonse always talked like that.

'Come and tell us all about it,' said Scaredy Cat. 'Perhaps we can help you.'

Alphonse looked at his friend, sat down and told his story. 'The trouble is,' he began, 'I have got to move house, and find somewhere else to live, I have, I have,' he wailed. 'Mr Brown has arranged for some men to come and repair the organ. It's not really working very well, and some of the pipes have sprung a leak, they have, they have. To put it right the men will have to take it all to bits, and I shall lose my little home, I will, I will. I suppose it will be better afterwards, because it will not be so draughty, and then I shall be very cosy again. But where can I go while the repairs are being done?' Oh dear, oh dear, I'm in real trouble, I am, I am.'

'I didn't know about this at all,' said Scaredy Cat. 'I can see that you can't stay here while the repairs are being done. But I can't think of anywhere you could stay for the time being. There's always the vicarage, I suppose, but I don't think Mr Brown or his wife will be very happy about that, and they might expect me to chase you out again.'

'Couldn't you find Alphonse a small hole somewhere?'

asked the Stone Angel. 'There must be lots of little holes in a big church like this. He could move into one of those and be quite safe until the organ has been repaired.'

Following the Stone Angel's advice Scaredy Cat spent the next two days searching the church diligently for suitable small holes for Alphonse to live in. He found several, of course, but none seemed right for the job. Some were too big, and they would be cold and draughty, some were too small and even a tiny mouse like Alphonse would have a struggle to get in. Some were too obvious, and people might poke in them, and some looked very dusty and dirty. Then Scaredy Cat spotted one that looked just right.

The hole he saw was right under the front pew at the front end of the church. It was quite close to where the organ was, so the move would not be too far. Being at the front, nobody ever sat in the pew, so Alphonse would be left undisturbed all the time.

The next day, Scaredy Cat told Alphonse all about it. When he took Alphonse to see it, he had second thoughts, because it was a very tiny hole, but Alphonse was delighted. He crept inside and looked around. Then he came out again. 'It's just right for me,' he squeaked, 'it is, it is. Once inside it is quite large, really, and it doesn't matter if the opening is small because I am small too. Us church mice are very poor you know, and we don't have much to eat, we don't, we don't. We don't grow very big, we're really very small and thin. Thank you so very much, thank you, thank you,' squeaked Alphonse again.

So it was arranged that the next day Scaredy Cat helped Alphonse to carry all his belongings to his new home. He couldn't carry much because Alphonse's belongings were not very big, and he had to carry them in his mouth, but he managed it eventually.

Later that week the men arrived to start work on the organ. They seemed to take a long time. One of the men looked at the great bellows in the organ and declared that it looked as if a mouse had been nibbling them. Scaredy Cat chuckled to himself, thinking of Alphonse.

When he got the chance to talk to the Stone Angel once again, he asked him about the story of the Good Samaritan once more.

'It was a story that Jesus told,' said the Stone Angel. 'A poor man was attacked on a road, and left half-dead. Three people came from the man's own country along the road, but none of them stopped to help him. Perhaps they were all afraid. Then the Samaritan, a man from another country, came by. He stopped to help him.'

'I think that Christians should always help one another,' declared Scaredy Cat.

'Not only other Christians but everybody who needs help should be given it by us,' replied the Stone Angel. 'Just as you helped Alphonse. Which reminds me, has he settled back in his house again, now that the men have finished?'

'Oh yes,' said Scaredy Cat. 'He says that he is much warmer now, and he's very thankful for all that we have done for him.'

The Stone Angel smiled quietly to himself. Now he felt his family were all safe and secure once more.

Think about . . .

Think about what it must be like to be ignored by people. It can happen at school, or out on the street. How do you feel if you are ignored?

Pray about . . .

Dear God,
   I wish people
   were more like
   the Good Samaritan.

He crossed the road
   and helped someone
   he didn't even know
   in a place
   where he could have been
   in danger.

There are so many people
   who are ignored
   or forgotten, God.
And they shouldn't be.

Dear God,
   help us all
   to cross over the road
   and be Good Samaritans.

Amen.

THE HOLE

Scaredy Cat learns more about the Bible.

One Sunday morning Scaredy Cat, as he usually did, went into the church for the morning service. At the end of the service he quickly ran out of the church again, down the path to the back of the church. Then he sat down on the path and laughed and laughed and laughed to himself. Alphonse, it appeared, had been at it again he thought!

During the service, one of the men had stood up in order to read a passage from the Bible as usual. Scaredy Cat always listened carefully to this because he found that he could learn a great deal. On this particular morning, however, instead of using the large Bible at the front of the church, the man picked up one of the small Bibles from the back of the church. When he opened it he had found that the page he wanted to read from had actually been gnawed through by something or someone, leaving a large hole through the page, thus destroying some of the words. The poor man had had no time to get another Bible, so he had continued to read, but tried to fill in the missing words so that it all made sense. Using his memory, he read very well, thought Scaredy Cat, until he came to one sentence about the Stilling of the Storm, when he read 'Master save us, we're going to float!'

The poor man reading the passage realised that he had made a terrible mistake and he tried to correct it. He read again, 'Master save us we're going to swim!' It sounded even worse than before, and the man had sat down promptly. It could be no other than Alphonse, who loved to nibble things.

Scaredy Cat went back into the church later on to talk to his old friend the Stone Angel. They laughed about the hole in the Bible which had made the reader make such a mistake. But the matter had made Scaredy Cat think.

'Why is the Bible so important?' he asked. 'Why does it have to be read at each service and exactly what is the Bible anyway?'

The Stone Angel took a deep breath. 'That's three questions,' he said, 'and they will take a lot of explaining. The Bible is really a collection of many books, some long and some short. They were written a long time ago, some of them perhaps three or four thousand years ago. The latest must be nearly two thousand years old. They tell the story of the Jewish nation for many years, and also the life story of Jesus, God's Son. They include letters and poems. They are very important.'

'Why are they important?' asked Scaredy Cat.

'Well, not only do they tell us about the Jewish nation and of Jesus and how the early church started, but they are really God's words for us today,' replied the Stone Angel. 'They are a guide to help us to understand things, and tell us how we should live. They tell us what things we should believe and do.'

'Is that why we should always read them?' asked Scaredy Cat again. 'Or in my case, listen to them?'

'Yes it is,' replied the Stone Angel. 'If you listen to them, the stories they tell and the advice they give and the things they suggest, you will learn more about our Heavenly Father and what things please him. You will learn to love him more.'

Scaredy Cat sat and thought about this for a long time. He could see now just how important the Bible really was, although he still thought that Alphonse's nibbling act in the old Bible was very funny. 'I hope,' thought Scaredy Cat, 'that God laughs, because I do it a lot!'

Outside, Scaredy Cat met Ginger Tom. They talked together about the Bible stories while they waited for their dinner. 'I like stories,' said Ginger Tom, 'and I can learn a lot from them. I wish I knew more of the stories in the Bible.'

'I like stories, too,' said Scaredy Cat, 'and I do know quite a few stories from the Bible. As I hear them I try to remember them, and to remember what they sometimes mean. Perhaps I could begin to teach you some of the stories from the Bible, though I might make a few mistakes sometimes. I once told a story to Alphonse and got John the Baptist and Judas Iscariot mixed up!'

So it was agreed that every afternoon, after their sleep after dinner time, the two cats would find a quiet spot in the garden and settle down together. Then Scaredy Cat began to tell Ginger Tom some of the Bible stories as he remembered them. Sometimes he did get things mixed up or forgot part of the story but he generally got most of it right. Occasionally Ginger Tom asked questions, and sometimes he even told Scaredy Cat stories that he had heard also.

After some time the two friends began to enjoy their daily session of story telling. Some of the other animals began to come along and listen too, and soon the group included two or three other cats, a couple of dogs, one or two sparrows and even a hedgehog! The Bible stories began to spread far and wide.

Much later on, the Stone Angel asked Scaredy Cat how his Bible story telling was progressing. 'Do you have a new story every day, or do you tell the same story several times over?' he asked.

'Oh they often ask for the same stories again and again,' replied Scaredy Cat. 'They love the stories of Jesus and how he healed people. They also listen to the stories of David and Goliath again and again. I seem to make them longer each time I tell them!'

'Well done,' said the Stone Angel. 'The more you tell the stories the more people will learn to love our Heavenly Father, and know just how much he loves them.'

Think about . . .

How many stories can you remember from the Bible?
Which are your favourites and why?

Pray about . . .

Dear God,
   this Bible book
   is brilliant!

There are loads
   of stories in it.

Some are really exciting,
   like David and Goliath,
   and Moses escaping from Egypt.

Some make you think,
   and others are scary.

But I love it, God.
I learn so much
   from these stories.
I learn about you.

Thank you God.

Amen.

THE BURGLARS

*Scaredy Cat learns that Christians help others
and try to put right things that are wrong.*

Scaredy Cat had been dozing for quite a long time during
the night. He dreamed of all the things he liked: large fish
suppers, jugs of cream, lying in the sun and playing with
Ginger Tom. He had just dreamed of another large fish supper waiting for him on his plate, when – plop! the dream
exploded, and Scaredy Cat found himself wide awake.
'That's strange,' he thought, 'what has woken me up?'
Scaredy Cat listened for a while, but the house seemed quiet
and still, no one was getting up in the bedrooms and there
was no running water. So he settled down to sleep again.

Suddenly he woke up with a start once more, and sat up
in his box under the table. This time he was quite sure
that he had heard a strange sound. He pricked up his ears
and listened again, very carefully. There, he heard it again.
What was it and where was it coming from? Deciding to
go and investigate, he slowly and quietly crept out of his
box and looked around the kitchen. There was nothing
unexpected there. Then he trotted into the living room of
the vicarage, but all seemed well in there too. He crossed
the hall, and then he heard the sound again. This time he
was sure where the noise was coming from – Mr Brown's
study!

At first Scaredy Cat thought that Mr Brown must be
working very late, but then he realised that there was no light
on in the study. He knew that the vicar couldn't see in the
dark. Then through the crack on the edge of the door, he
spied a light shining around just like a torch. He could hear
drawers being opened and papers being shuffled around.
He even heard the sound of low voices talking in whispers.

It then flashed through Scaredy Cat's mind that they had some unexpected visitors – burglars. Scaredy Cat wondered what he should do. He could hardly burst into the room and arrest them! They wouldn't take any notice of him, and would only laugh at his miaow. He couldn't open the door anyway, no matter how hard he tried. He thought about going back into the kitchen and knocking something noisy onto the floor, but he thought that he might make more trouble and smash things that were valuable. Then he had another brainwave.

Creeping quietly down the hall to the stairs, he quickly climbed up the stairs to the landing on the next floor. He knew which bedroom was used by Mr and Mrs Brown but when he reached it, however, he found that it was firmly shut. His idea of trying to wake them did not seem such a good one after all.

All he could do was sit outside the door, and begin to miaow for help. He miaowed long and loud in the hope that the noise would be heard through the thick wood door. After some minutes with no apparent success, Scaredy Cat heard a noise in the bedroom.

Mrs Brown suddenly opened the door and peered out looking for Scaredy Cat in the dark. 'Scaredy Cat,' she whispered, 'what's the matter?' Scaredy Cat jumped on her feet to tell her where he was. Mrs Brown bent down to stroke him, and then to pick him up. 'What's disturbed you?' she asked.

Scaredy Cat turned from her grasp and ran part of the way down the stairs again. Mrs Brown stood looking at him, seeing only his green eyes shining in the dark. She began to return to the bedroom, so Scaredy Cat ran back up the stairs, and charged into her again. Then he turned round and began to run down the stairs again. Slowly Mrs Brown realised that Scaredy Cat wanted her to go down the stairs. Slowly, stumbling in the dark, for she did not bother to put the light on, Mrs Brown crept down the stairs trying to follow the cat.

When she arrived at the bottom of the stairs, Scaredy Cat ran to the door of the study and began to miaow very loudly. Mystified, Mrs Brown followed him slowly, and then she let out a gasp. There was somebody in the study! Trembling with fright, she opened the door and switched on the light.

Scaredy Cat could see immediately that the window in the study was open, and two men were standing over Mr Brown's desk shuffling through his papers. He heard one man say, 'There doesn't seem to be any money here; they're as poor as church mice!' Then the room was flooded with light. Mrs Brown stood there and just screamed and screamed. The two men dived towards the window, and jumped quickly through it. The next moment they were gone.

A few moments later Mr Brown came running down the stairs and into his study. He threw his arms around his wife to comfort her and stop her crying. All that Mrs Brown could say was 'Scaredy Cat woke me up. He knew what was happening.'

The next few hours were pandemonium in the vicarage. The children came racing down the stairs also making a great deal of clatter and shouting at the top of their voices. Mr Brown called the police who came racing along with their lovely noisy police cars. Scaredy Cat overheard that these were the detectives. They searched the grounds outside as well as inside the rooms. Scaredy Cat watched with growing interest as they looked for clues and took fingerprints in the room. Then everybody had to have their own fingerprints taken as well – 'for elimination' one detective said. Scaredy Cat was disappointed that they didn't seem to need his! There were people coming and going all the time, and the police knocked up all the neighbours to see if they had been burgled as well. One family, three doors away, had been, so all the police trooped down to their house also. After a while, peace began to settle on the vicarage once more. Mr Brown picked up Scaredy Cat and gave him a cuddle. 'You are our clever Scaredy Cat,' he said. 'You heard those men and you warned us what was happening! I think you'll have to join the police force as a detective!' Scaredy Cat's chest swelled with pride.

It was much later the next day before Scaredy Cat went to report to the Stone Angel in church as he had spent the morning watching the man from next door come and repair the window which the two men had forced open. So he told the Stone Angel all about what had happened.

'Well done, my friend,' said the Stone Angel. 'Christians should always be on the alert, watching out for signs of trouble or danger. In that way you can help others and keep guard. We are always being tempted to do wrong things. Praying to our Heavenly Father helps us to keep watchful.'

'Perhaps I could guard the church as well as the vicarage!' thought Scaredy Cat.

Think about . . .

Are there times when you want to do something that you know you shouldn't? What kind of things are you thinking when you feel like this? Is this wrong or right?

Pray about . . .

Dear God,
   sometimes
   I want to do things
   that I know I shouldn't.

It's usually
   only small things
   like taking a biscuit
   from the kitchen
   or watching something on TV
   that my parents wouldn't like.

Why do I feel like this, God?
Does it mean I'm really bad?

I don't mean to,
   which is why I'm telling you now.
And that's good isn't it?

Help me, God,
   not to give in,
   even though I know
   how delicious
   those biscuits
   can be!

Amen.

MILK ROUND

Scaredy Cat learns the danger of greed.

The day was both hot and dry. Scaredy Cat, who loved the sunshine, had spent all the morning in the garden, basking in the heat. Now he wandered back into the house again. He felt dry and thirsty, so he went over to his dish to have a drink of water. When he reached the dish, however, he found that he had already drunk it dry. He continued to wander round the kitchen searching for water but found not a drop, and even though the weather was beautiful, he did need a drink. So he kept looking and it got hotter and hotter.

He wandered round the garden again, still looking for something to drink, but to no avail. Often one of the drainpipes was dripping with water, but today they were completely dry. There were no puddles, no pools, no streams in the garden; nothing. Sighing deeply, Scaredy Cat went back indoors.

He jumped up onto the work surface of the kitchen, a thing he was not allowed to do, in search of something to quench his thirst. There, at the end of the surface, sat a big jug of milk. Mrs Brown had poured a bottle of milk into it sometime before, but had forgotten to put it into the fridge. So it sat there, cool and inviting.

Scaredy Cat hesitated. He was certainly thirsty, and a nice drink of milk was just what he wanted, but he knew that it would be wrong to touch it. He should wait until Mrs Brown poured him some into his dish, but she wasn't there. The trouble was he was convinced that if he didn't have a drink soon, he would die of thirst, and then Mrs Brown wouldn't have a cat to give a drink! If he just had one little sip of the milk, he thought, she would never notice, and he would have quenched his thirst.

He sat and watched the jug of milk. There was not a sound in the vicarage. Scaredy Cat made up his mind. He stood up, put his two front paws on the milk jug, and tried to scramble up the side of the jug, but it was too high and slippery. Then, in his struggle, he felt the jug beginning to rock slowly on the surface. Suddenly it slipped and fell over with a crash, and Scaredy Cat saw the milk spill all over the place. Not knowing what else to do, he began to lap up the milk, convinced that he was saving Mrs Brown the job of cleaning it up later.

A short while later, the jug still lay on its side with much of the milk running all over the place, and Scaredy Cat still trying to clean it all away. He was beginning to enjoy himself, and no longer felt as thirsty as he did before. He'd had enough milk for his needs, but kept on greedily drinking it all up. 'After all,' thought Scaredy Cat, 'it would be a shame to waste it all.' He stuck his head inside the jug and continued to drink on until it was nearly all gone. He now felt so full that he seemed to have grown twice his real size, and his tummy felt as though it was about to burst.

At that moment Scaredy Cat heard a sound and knew that Mrs Brown had now returned from wherever it was she had been. He quickly decided that it would be wise to retreat and hide somewhere till her expected anger and wrath had calmed down.

Then he realised his mistake. First of all Mrs Brown walked straight into the kitchen and caught him. Secondly, he found he could not get out of the milk jug again; he was stuck!

With Mrs Brown scolding him loudly, Scaredy Cat tried to shake himself free of the jug. He stood up, with his body out through the neck of the jug, but with his head firmly stuck inside it. He tried to shake himself free, but all he did was to bang the jug on the work surface, making an awful noise, and spilling the remaining milk everywhere.

He miaowed loudly, and called for help, but Mrs Brown seemed to erupt with laughter at the sight of poor Scaredy Cat caught in such a mess. He turned round and round and threshed about wildly, but to no avail. He was well and truly stuck!

'It serves you right,' shouted Mrs Brown at him. 'If you had waited and not been so greedy, I would have given you a drink, and you wouldn't be in this mess. Now, how on earth am I going to be able to free you?'

She grasped poor Scaredy Cat round his body and tried to prise his head out of the jug, but all to no avail. She tried putting some butter round the edge of the jug, so that his head would slide out, but that did not work either. Then she thought for a minute. 'Scaredy Cat,' she ordered, 'keep still. I'll be back in a minute, I'm just going to get something to help you.'

Scaredy Cat didn't like the sound of that. He sat still but grew more and more impatient. He couldn't hear anything at all, and he certainly couldn't see. What was Mrs Brown doing, he wondered?

When she returned, Scaredy Cat realised that she had been in the garage and had brought with her a large hammer.

'This was my favourite milk jug,' she declared, 'but I shall have to sacrifice it for your sake.' Scaredy Cat wondered, uneasily, what she meant.

Grasping him firmly round his body, Scaredy Cat heard the most horrendous bang. Then, suddenly, he was free; he was out of the jug! He opened his eyes and saw the broken pieces of the milk jug all round him, and the remains of the milk dripping everywhere. Mrs Brown stood there with the hammer in her hand.

At first Scaredy Cat thought that she might be tempted to use the hammer on him! He decided to make himself scarce for the time being.

Later on he wandered into the church and to chat to his friend, the Stone Angel. 'I don't feel very hungry at the moment,' he admitted to the Stone Angel, as he told him all about his adventures again.

'It serves you right,' said the Stone Angel. 'You have shown yourself to be very greedy, and you weren't prepared to wait for the milk. Greedy Christians come in all sorts of shapes and sizes you know. You can be greedy with your food, and want more than is good for you. Some people can be greedy with money, and crave for more and more, with no idea how to use it wisely and well. Some others are greedy for sleep, and spend all their time in bed! They never seem to achieve anything.'

'Oh dear,' said Scaredy Cat. 'I never knew how easy it was to be greedy, or how many ways you could show it.'

'Well take it as a warning,' replied the Stone Angel. 'The only kind of greediness you should have is to love our Heavenly Father more and more, and to help others when they need it.'

'I think I've learned my lesson,' admitted Scaredy Cat as he turned and wandered outside, feeling very full, rather ill, and just a little silly.

Think about . . .

There are a lot of people in this world who have very little to eat. Why do you think this is? How does this make you feel?

Pray about . . .

Dear God,
   sometimes I can be greedy.

I put too much on my plate
   at tea time and then end up
   not being able to finish it.

Then Mum or Dad says,
   'Your eyes are too big
   for your stomach!'

Being greedy can even
   make me feel a bit sick.
Like when I eat too many sweets.

It makes me think about all those
   who never have a chance
   to put a little extra on their plate.
They have little to eat
   and we have so much.

It's not fair, God.
We should share our food
   so that everyone has something to eat.

Help us to do that, God.

Amen.

The Wedding

Scaredy Cat learns the true meaning of marriage and the importance of the promises.

Excitement filled the vicarage; there was to be a wedding! Scaredy Cat was very interested. He had never been to a wedding, so he didn't really know what it was all about. As usual he went to consult his friend the Stone Angel, in church.

The Stone Angel told him that when two people fall in love and decide to spend the rest of their lives together, there has to be a wedding. 'At the wedding,' he said, 'the two people promise to love and care for each other, and share together the good times and the bad, "in sickness and in health" for the rest of their lives.'

'Sounds good to me,' said Scaredy Cat, 'perhaps I could get married some day.'

'Well you will have to find somebody willing to put up with your mischief,' joked the Stone Angel.

Scaredy Cat left the Stone Angel and went off to think about it for a while. In the meantime, Mr Brown said that he had to call the 'banns'. 'I wonder what banns are,' thought Scaredy Cat. 'Why does he want to go banning people when they want to get married? Weddings seem to be rather complicated,' he thought, as he wandered off into the garden to find his favourite place to lie in the sun.

A few days later the couple, who had been to see Mr Brown before, came to the church with two or three other people. Scaredy Cat went into the church to see what was going on, and he found that they were having a kind of rehearsal of the ceremony. Mr Brown told them where to stand, and what to say at the different times in the service. He even showed them how to walk up and down the aisle, which made Scaredy Cat laugh; he thought all adults knew how to walk!

'Why do they need to practice?' asked Scaredy Cat.

'Well,' said the Stone Angel, 'a wedding is a very important thing in people's life. They don't want to make a mistake with anything, so all the people involved have a little practice to make sure that they have got everything right.'

'But what I can't understand,' said Scaredy Cat, 'is why there has to be a best man. I thought the best man was the man getting married, but it's not in this wedding, is it?'

The Stone Angel took a deep breath. 'The best man is usually a friend of the man getting married – the groom. He is there to help him, and he holds the ring until it is needed,' explained the Stone Angel. 'He's the best man for the job!'

'I think I see,' said Scaredy Cat. 'But why does the bride have to be "given away"?'

'Oh dear,' thought the Stone Angel, 'this is going to get complicated.' He looked down at Scaredy Cat and continued. 'The man who gives the bride away is usually the father of the bride. He is the one responsible for her until he gives her away to the man she wishes to marry – the groom.'

'Oh dear,' said Scaredy Cat. 'I don't think I'll bother getting married. It's much too complicated!'

On the day of the wedding Mr Brown told Scaredy Cat to keep out of the way because everyone would be too busy to worry about him. 'No fear,' thought Scaredy Cat, 'I'm going to watch this and see what I can learn.'

The church was very full of people because the two getting married were members of the church, and so they were well known to many people there. All the men dressed up in their best suits, and the ladies wore hats that left Scaredy Cat helpless with laughter. To him, most of them looked like peculiar peacocks! Mr Brown's wife was there with Susan and David who were all enjoying the day, which had turned out nice and sunny. Scaredy Cat had never seen Mrs Brown in a hat before either, and it seemed to wobble all the time. The children were on their best behaviour, which was also unusual.

There were people coming and going all the time, and the organ was playing some very enjoyable music. Then suddenly everybody stood up and the bride came down the aisle on the arm of the man who wanted to give her away. She was dressed in a long white dress.

Everybody sang the hymns and listened to the young couple make their promises to each other. Scaredy Cat thoroughly enjoyed the whole affair. The church itself had been filled with flowers, so many in fact, that they made him sneeze.

That was how everybody first noticed Scaredy Cat. 'Oh look,' they said, 'a black cat!' Well he wasn't completely black, he had a small patch of white on him, but not much. Then to his surprise, at the end of the wedding he was picked up and stroked by several ladies who then took him and placed him in the arms of the bride. He even had his photo taken like that. Scaredy Cat was very pleased with himself, and some said that he was a good sign.

Later that evening Scaredy Cat and the Stone Angel talked together about the events of the day. 'It was a very enjoyable wedding,' said the Stone Angel, and Scaredy Cat agreed with him. 'It reminds me of the story of Jesus attending a wedding,' said the Stone Angel, and Scaredy Cat sat up, listening carefully.

'Jesus and his disciples enjoyed a good wedding, and one day they were all invited to one. There were so many people there that they ran out of wine used in the celebrations. Jesus told some people to fill up the big pots with water, and use that for the wine. When they poured it out they found it had turned into real wine.'

'I hope they all enjoyed it,' said Scaredy Cat as he nibbled at a few crumbs of wedding cake that had been given to him. 'I know I did.'

Think about . . .

What do you think about marriage? Do you think it is easy or difficult to be married? Why do you think people get married?

Pray about . . .

Dear God,
    I know I'm young
    and that it will be
    a very long time
    before I get married,
    but can we talk about it anyway?

I think it is amazing
    that you can love someone
    so much
    that you want
    to spend the rest of your life
    with them!

It's brilliant!

I know that it must be hard,
    and at times you may argue
    or disagree,
    but if you still love each other
    it is even better
    than having a best friend!

Dear God,
    I hope that if I get married
    you will help me
    make it a brilliant one.

Amen.

THE KITE

Scaredy Cat learns to think for himself and not let others talk him into doing foolish things.

It was a lovely windy day and Scaredy Cat was sitting watching the leaves blow about as the branches of the trees gently swayed in the breeze, and the smaller bushes and plants nearly bent double with the force of the gusts. Even the fur on his coat was waving about, and once he heard the sound of a milk bottle falling over and smashing onto the ground. After a while, Scaredy Cat decided to go for a walk and as he turned a corner of the vicarage he was nearly blown off his feet with the force of the wind blowing down the narrow passageway.

Scaredy Cat heard the sound of excited voices. He knew that the children were with all the others from the nearby houses and were in the garden next door, playing their own games. He quickly climbed the fence between them to watch their antics and saw . . . a kite! It was a lovely green thing, with lots of ribbons and strings coming from one end. It lay on the grass, but bumped and bounced about with a mind and will of its own just as if it were alive. It seemed to do exactly what it felt like doing, for whatever the children tried to do they could not seem to control it, never mind get it up into the air! It flipped this way and that, and never seemed able to keep still. Scaredy Cat sat for ages, watching the kite and the children, who were laughing and screaming at their failure to control it. They were having a lovely time, and Scaredy Cat wished he could play with them. Then they all heard a voice calling out to the children telling them it was time to come into the house and eat.

At first the children were not sure what to do with the

kite, but then one of the older ones took the cord attached to the kite and tied it to a nearby tree. It was now safe and secure so the children trooped into the house.

After a short time the wind died down a little and the kite settled on the ground and lay still, as there was no wind to bring it alive again. This was too good an opportunity for Scaredy Cat to miss! He climbed down off his perch on the fence and crept slowly towards the kite.

It was a lovely kite. There were several different coloured ribbons attached to it, and the kite itself had a lovely face painted on it. To Scaredy Cat it almost looked as if it was grinning at him. Scaredy Cat began to play with the coloured ribbons which occasionally fluttered in the breeze. He patted and played football with them, and then jumped and bounced on them as if they were a mouse to be played with. He held them in his paws and tried to run off with them, but of course he couldn't get very far.

Then suddenly, to his surprise, the face on the kite opened its mouth and whispered, 'Hello, cat. Do you like playing with me?'

'Oooh, yes,' said Scaredy Cat after he had got over his surprise of hearing the kite talk. 'I'm having a lovely time. I wish the wind would blow just a little bit harder again, and then I could watch you flying.'

'Oh, but you can,' replied the kite. 'I haven't been tied very tightly, and when the wind blows strongly just hold tight to my ribbons and wait and see; I'm sure I shall be free again.'

Sure enough, after a few minutes the wind began to blow strongly again, and the kite lifted up off the ground, bumping up and down. Scaredy Cat thought that this was wonderful, and he held tightly to the ribbons from the kite. Then, just as the kite expected, the wind began to blow fiercely, and the kite rose up high into the sky. With the strain on the cord, it suddenly snapped, and the wind took the kite high up into the air. Scaredy Cat watched his friend the kite swoop and zoom all over the place, but he forgot to let go, and suddenly he found himself being picked up off the ground as the kite flew higher and higher.

Up and up they went, with Scaredy Cat hanging onto the ribbon for dear life. Soon he was as high as the hedges, and soon as high as the small trees. It was great fun, as he could see more and more from his increasingly dangerous position. Up and up he went, higher and higher with the wind blowing stronger than ever.

As Scaredy Cat looked down, he realised for the first time that he was in trouble; the kite was now flying higher and higher and totally out of control. Scaredy Cat was now level with the church roof, and he started to feel very afraid. If he let go, he would fall a long way, but if he held on, the kite might take him miles and miles away, and then how could he ever get back?

He realised the danger he was in, and he cried out for help, but of course no one thought of looking up to see a small cat clinging for dear life onto a runaway kite.

As they flew over the top of the church, the wind quietened down a little and the kite began to drop lower. The church roof was now looming up very close to Scaredy Cat, and he realised that he was going to collide with it.

The kite seemed to swoop down lower and lower, and then Scaredy Cat saw the roof of the church only just beneath his feet. He closed his eyes and let go . . .

He felt a bump beneath him, as he landed safely on the church roof. The kite was flying away now, and he was sure he could hear it laughing. Scaredy Cat was not very pleased. The roof of the church was quite steep, but he managed to scramble down it, to reach the guttering below. From there he crept along until he found a drainpipe, and was able to slowly slide down it to the ground and safety; what an adventure!

Walking slowly into the church, Scaredy Cat was unaware of the look on the Stone Angel's face; a mix of concern and amusement. 'Ah', said the Stone Angel, 'I saw you coming in, in a very unusual way. That was a rather foolish thing to do, because you could have easily been hurt.'

'I know,' said Scaredy Cat rather sheepishly. 'I didn't intend it to happen, but the kite talked me into holding on.' And so it was that the Stone Angel listened as Scaredy Cat told all that had happened.

'You know,' said the Stone Angel, 'it is always wise to listen to others you can trust, but you must learn not to let others talk you into doing naughty or dangerous things. You must think for yourself. Christians must learn to stop and think. It is so easy to let someone else talk you into doing wrong and silly things. You must be strong enough to learn to say no!'

'I see what you mean,' replied Scaredy Cat, remembering how afraid he had been. 'I'll learn to be more careful in future,' and with that, he settled down at the bottom of the Stone Angel's pillar and drifted off to sleep.

Think about . . .

Have you ever been tempted to do something because everyone else was doing it, even though you knew it might be wrong, or silly or maybe even dangerous?

Pray about . . .

Dear God,
    sometimes it is easier
    to do what everyone else
    is doing.

Like at school
    if people are making fun of someone,
    it can be easier to join in
    rather than help the other person.

Sometimes
    it only takes one person
    to persuade you
    to do what they're doing
    even though
    you don't want to.

I need to think for myself more,
    and not be easily led.
Help me do that, God.

Amen.

CHEERING UP

Scaredy Cat learns how he can help others.

Scaredy Cat sat quietly in the churchyard, watching; there was a funeral in the church, and the coffin was being taken into the church with lots of flowers on it, and a lot of people were following.

Eventually, everyone filed out of the church and were soon sitting in the large black cars, which drove slowly away to the cemetery.

Scaredy Cat had seen many funerals in the church; some of them had only one or two people there, and others with quite a lot of people. Scaredy Cat knew because the Stone Angel had told him, that sometimes the person who died had come from a large family, but the ones Scaredy Cat felt most sorry for were those where there was hardly any family left at all. He remembered one funeral where no one at all followed the coffin, but Mr Brown insisted on a full funeral service 'in case somebody came along'.

In this particular funeral service, Scaredy Cat knew some of the people there; they were members of the church, so Scaredy Cat saw them quite often. The person who had died was the husband of a lovely lady from church; she often spoilt Scaredy Cat by bringing him biscuits on Sundays before church started. As they were Christians they had happy joyful hymns; 'a real thanksgiving service', Mr Brown had said. Scaredy Cat felt that he was a part of the family too, and tried as best he could to sing along.

He went along later to talk to his friend the Stone Angel all about this. 'When a Christian dies,' said the Stone Angel in answer to Scaredy Cat's many questions, 'we all know that although they have left this earth, they are now with our Heavenly Father.'

'Is that why people sing happy hymns?' asked Scaredy Cat.

'Yes, that's right,' replied the Stone Angel. 'People want to say thank you for all the great things the person has done. The family is sad that one of them has gone, and they miss them, but they are also contented because that person is in heaven with our Father.'

Scaredy Cat went back home thinking hard about this. 'If you are a Christian,' he thought, 'then you have everything to look forward to,' and this cheered him up.

A few days later Scaredy Cat went into the church for a chat to the Stone Angel. He had hardly been in the place for more than a minute, when he heard a small noise. He turned round to see what it was, and was very surprised to see an old lady coming into the church. Scaredy Cat recognised her immediately; she was the wife of the man who had died recently.

The old lady sat down quietly in one of the pews, and began to pray. Scaredy Cat left her alone, and went to the Stone Angel. 'I think that you may have a small job to do in a few moments,' said the Stone Angel in a quiet voice to Scaredy Cat.

'Who? Me?' said Scaredy Cat. He couldn't understand what the Stone Angel was talking about. What job could he possibly do? Then he heard another sound, and this time it came from the old lady sitting in the pew. Scaredy Cat sat and listened for a moment, and then realised that the old lady was quietly crying. He quickly realised the situation. 'Oh dear,' he thought, 'she is missing her husband very much, and she feels very unhappy. Perhaps she doesn't realise that he must now be with our Heavenly Father.'

In a flash Scaredy Cat realised what the Stone Angel had been talking about. Perhaps he could help the old lady, and give her some sort of comfort. Perhaps he could remind her that her husband was with God.

Without any more thought Scaredy Cat trotted down the church to where the old lady was sitting. She had her eyes shut, but the tears were rolling down her cheeks. She sounded very miserable and unhappy. 'Miaow,' said Scaredy Cat. The old lady opened her eyes in surprise, although she could hardly see out of them.

'Oh, Scaredy Cat,' she said, 'This is a surprise.'

Without any further hesitation Scaredy Cat jumped up onto her lap and gently rubbed his head against her hands. 'Miaow,' he said again, really meaning 'Cheer up!' The old lady gently stroked him, and nursed him in her arms. This was something Scaredy Cat usually enjoyed anyway, but this time he tried to comfort the old lady, and show her that he wanted to be her friend. As she sat there stroking him, she began to stop crying, and she fumbled in her pocket to find her handkerchief. Drying her eyes, she then sat quietly cuddling Scaredy Cat, who relaxed and purred contentedly; he was bringing some comfort and happiness to the old lady.

She glanced at her watch and gasped. 'Oh dear, just look at the time. I must go.' Then she looked down at

Scaredy Cat lying still in her arms. 'Thank you, Scaredy Cat,' she said. 'You have brought me a lot of comfort and I now know that I'm not alone in the world at all.' She gently put Scaredy Cat down on the floor, and watched him trot up to the Stone Angel. She smiled gently and again said, 'Thank you.' Then she got up and went outside.

'I told you that you had a job to do,' said the Stone Angel to Scaredy Cat. 'You brought a great deal of comfort and happiness to the old lady, and you have also made her your friend. That will help her a great deal now and stop her from being so lonely.'

'Thank you, said Scaredy Cat. 'Perhaps that's one job that Christians can do for each other. We can show to each other our Heavenly Father's love.'

Think about . . .

There will have been times when people have helped you if you were upset, and you have probably helped others too. Why is this good?

Pray about . . .

Dear God,
    when I'm upset
    and someone asks how I am,
    it makes me feel cared for
    and loved.

And when I see
    someone who is upset
    and I try to help them,
    I want them to know
    that I care
    and love them too.

Perhaps, God,
    if everyone cared a little more
    about each other,
    and gave each other hugs
    when upset,
    then everyone would be happier.

Wouldn't the world
    be wonderful?

Help us try to make it
    like that, God.

Amen.

ON HOLIDAY

Scaredy Cat learns how to make more friends and to tell them about his Heavenly Father.

Scaredy Cat was very excited; he was going on holiday! At least, strictly speaking Mr and Mrs Brown and the children were going on holiday. Scaredy Cat realised that he couldn't be left there by himself, so he must also be going somewhere. He had watched as the suitcases were being packed and Mr Brown had spent ages poring over maps of roads to various places. The car had been taken to the garage to be 'serviced' Mr Brown had said, and was now being carefully cleaned and polished. It looked beautiful, better than Scaredy Cat could ever remember it. Mrs Brown had been taking out of drawers all kinds of clothes that he had never seen before, and packing them into the cases. Books had been carefully selected to go with them, and magazines and sweets and all sorts of other things. The children also packed up some of their toys and games in case they got bored while on holiday.

One thing puzzled Scaredy Cat, however. So far no one had mentioned anything to him about what would happen to him! No one had said where he would be staying. Perhaps he would go to the lady next door, and share with Ginger Tom. That would be nice, he thought, but that had never been mentioned either. Scaredy Cat began to feel rather worried about it all.

He decided that he had better go and talk it over with his friend the Stone Angel in church. The next day he trotted into the church and began to chat to him about all his fears and worries. 'What do you think will happen to me?' he asked. 'And where will I be sent to?'

'That's no problem,' said the Stone Angel. 'I expect that they will send you to the local cattery or cat's home.'

'What's that?' asked Scaredy Cat very mystified, and rather worried at the prospect.

'Many people round here have a cat or a dog,' said the Stone Angel. 'When they go away, they often put their dog into a kennel; that's a place where they look after dogs and other pets for a few days while their owners are away. Some of these places also look after cats, and they call them a cattery.'

'Oh, I see,' said Scaredy Cat. 'So someone else will be looking after me. What will it be like?'

'I believe it's very nice,' said the Stone Angel. 'You aren't allowed to wander off and go where you like, of course, because you'll never be able to find your way back again. But they will feed you well, and make sure that you are fit and comfortable at all times. I've heard very good reports of the local ones.'

'It sounds quite nice,' said Scaredy Cat. 'I'll let you know when I come back.'

Sure enough, the next day, Mrs Brown wrapped Scaredy Cat in an old blanket and put him in his usual box. The children packed some tins of his favourite food, and tucked him in comfortably. Then they went in the car to the cattery.

The lady who met them talked to Scaredy Cat, and stroked him gently. She seemed to understand cats and their needs. Then she took him down a long line of cages, many with other cats in them, and placed him gently in his own place. She put his own box and blanket into it also, so that Scaredy Cat felt more at home. She gave him some food and a small dish of water, and then wrote his name on a large card, which slotted into a place on the side of the cage. Scaredy Cat giggled to himself as she had trouble trying to spell it correctly. She introduced him to the cats on either side of him, and then left him to himself.

For a while Scaredy Cat felt a little bit lonely, and

wished that Ginger Tom or even the Stone Angel had been here to talk to, but he tried to settle down and enjoy his time there. After a while he decided to go and explore the place. The one end of the cage had a door in it which had been left open, so he wandered out of the cage. There was quite a large space for all the cats to walk around and get some exercise.

Later that day, Scaredy Cat decided to be polite and chat to his two neighbours. One was a rather proud Persian cat with a beautiful coat and lovely blue eyes. Her name was rather long and foreign sounding, and Scaredy Cat couldn't remember it. On the other side was a rather scruffy old tom cat called Charlie. While the Persian didn't seem very inclined to chat, Charlie did. They told each other all about themselves, and their adventures, and the things they had got up to. Scaredy Cat and Charlie became very good friends, and promised to see each other whenever they could.

As Scaredy Cat and Charlie talked, Scaredy Cat began to tell Charlie all about the church and Mr Brown and the Stone Angel. This was all new to Charlie and he listened very carefully.

Scaredy Cat also talked about God, and how he loved everyone, including cats, and how you could talk to him in prayer, and that he always listened and answered.

'Perhaps,' said Charlie hopefully, 'he will listen to me also if I talk to him in prayer.'

'I know he will,' said Scaredy Cat. 'When we get home we can see each other again, and we can talk some more about this.'

Each day the cats were fed regularly and given water to drink. As a treat some days, they had milk instead. Each day the lady came round and talked to them, and stroked them, and combed their fur and made sure that all was well. This must be like a beauty farm, thought Scaredy Cat!

Soon it was time to go home. Mrs Brown collected him, and made a great fuss of him. He said farewell to Charlie and the others, some of whom had become great friends to Scaredy Cat, and then they went home again.

Mr and Mrs Brown seemed to have enjoyed their holiday, and often talked about all the places they had visited. The children were quite excited at all the places they had seen and the people they had met. Mrs Brown had been in the sun, and her face was quite tanned.

As soon as he could Scaredy Cat went to see the Stone Angel. 'I've missed you,' said the Stone Angel. 'Did you have a good holiday? Was the cattery a good one?'

'Oh yes,' declared Scaredy Cat. He told the Stone Angel all about it, and what they did each day. He also told him about Charlie.

'You have made good use of your holiday, and told others of our Heavenly Father also. That is good because we need to tell others about him so that they can share his love as well,' said the Stone Angel. 'It's a pity that Stone Angels can't go on holiday also!'

Think about . . .

Jesus told people about God by telling stories. Are there stories you could tell people that would tell them about God?

Pray about . . .

Dear God,
   Jesus is a wonderful story teller
   isn't he?

I love the stories about him
   where there are crowds of people
   listening to him
   as he tells them
   about you
   and heaven
   and love!

Stories are great, God.
I wonder if I have any stories
   that I could tell people
   which would be about you?

I hope so.

Help me tell them, God.

Amen.

THE PIANIST

Scaredy Cat learns the importance of obedience.

When Scaredy Cat had first arrived at the vicarage, the one thing he had first learned was that he must never climb onto the furniture. Although he occasionally scrambled onto the settee for a quick snooze, when no one was looking, he was quickly taught never to climb onto chairs or tables or desks or anything in the house. Scaredy Cat always thought that this was a pity because in the kitchen there were often some lovely smells of food he would have liked to taste, but he always did as he was told, or nearly always.

One thing that Scaredy Cat always enjoyed was listening to Mrs Brown playing the old piano in the living room. She seemed to play some lovely tunes that made Scaredy Cat want to sing, and even dance to the music. As he watched her playing he always thought that he would like to try for himself, and it didn't seem to be too difficult. You just pressed the key and the right sound would come out, especially if you pressed several keys at once. Scaredy Cat wondered how long it would take to learn how to play, but he heard Mrs Brown say once to someone that she'd had to practise for many years. Scaredy Cat was sure that he could learn much more quickly than that.

One night, when everybody had long since gone to bed and the house was quiet and still, Scaredy Cat woke up from his slumbers on his bed underneath the kitchen table. He was not quite sure why he had woken up, but he didn't feel at all sleepy, so he got up and began to wander round the kitchen. Being a cat, he could see quite easily in the dark so he didn't bump into anything. He wandered through the door which always seemed to open easily and walked into the living room.

After running around for a while, he found nothing very exciting, and he was just thinking of going back to his bed in the kitchen, when he came to the old piano. As Scaredy Cat looked up, he quivered with excitement because Mrs Brown, who had been playing that evening, had left the lid of the piano open. Now was his chance to show everybody what a clever cat he was! He would play the piano!

Jumping onto a chair by the side of the piano Scaredy Cat sprang up, and looked carefully at the long line of black and white keys. Which were the high notes, and which were the low notes he wondered? Then there was the problem of the black keys. What did they do? He thought that they made notes as well, as he had seen Mrs Brown use them, but he was not quite sure. Ah well, he thought, I shall just have to experiment and see what happens.

Treading carefully, Scaredy Cat walked along the piano keys. To his delight, each time he pressed one with his paws it made a sound. This was wonderful! He raced down the keyboard, and then turned and raced back again, making such a glorious sound. He couldn't quite make out the tune he was playing, but it sounded fine. He

ran up and down the keys several times, and realised that at one end of the keys the notes were low, and at the other end they were high. He tried jumping up and down on them, playing several keys at once. 'This was lovely,' thought Scaredy Cat, really enjoying himself.

Suddenly he heard footsteps outside the door. The door swiftly opened, and the light was switched on. 'What on earth is going on?' cried Mr Brown. Then he suddenly stopped and laughed at Scaredy Cat. 'Scaredy Cat,' he said, 'you gave us all a great fright!' You woke us all up with your piano playing, and we thought that we had some musical burglars!'

He picked up Scaredy Cat and put him on the floor. Then he turned and closed the lid of the piano. 'There,' he said, 'that will stop your piano playing for tonight.' As he pushed Scaredy Cat back into the kitchen, he chuckled, 'I didn't realise that we had a musical cat! I have never heard of a cat playing the piano before.'

With that he went back upstairs, still chuckling to himself. 'At least,' thought Scaredy Cat, 'he seemed to think it was quite funny, and he didn't tell me off this time. I must try it again sometime, when I have the chance. They're bound to forget to close the piano lid some day!'

The next day both Mr and Mrs Brown continued to chuckle about their piano-playing cat, and to tease poor Scaredy Cat. Scaredy Cat didn't mind, because he liked everybody to be happy and cheerful.

As usual, the next day saw Scaredy Cat inside the church, telling the Stone Angel all about his adventures the night before, when he went piano playing. The Stone Angel also chuckled. 'You must have given the family an awful fright,' he said.

'They didn't know who it was,' said Scaredy Cat. 'I think they must have thought that they had a piano-playing ghost.'

'Nevertheless, there is a serious side to the matter,'

warned the Stone Angel. 'You have been taught not to climb onto the furniture, and you didn't do as you were told. Obedience is always important for Christians. The Bible has a story of a man who was told to go and speak with the people of a certain city. He refused to go, and ran in the other direction instead. He got himself into a lot of trouble as a result, and he ended up inside a great fish. His name was Jonah.'

'Gosh,' said Scaredy Cat. 'I think I would prefer to have the fish inside me!' He closed his eyes to dream of such a possibility.

Think about . . .

Can you think about any time when you have done something, even though you knew that you shouldn't? How does it make you feel now?

Pray about . . .

Dear God,
    I don't mean to be naughty
    or mischievous,
    but sometimes
    I can't help it!

I know that I get into trouble,
    and that I shouldn't have done it
    in the first place,
    but I still do it.

I do learn though, God.
Sometimes I get told off
    and that's not nice.
Or I upset people
    and that's not nice, either.

God,
    help me to do
    what I know is right,
    and not break the rules
    just because I want to.

Amen.

IN THE DARK

Scaredy Cat learns that we are given many gifts in order to use them to help others.

It had been a dark and stormy day, the wind howling round the house, and the leaves and branches blowing over the garden. The rain came down in torrents, and small streams and puddles appeared everywhere. There was not much light either and as the day began to draw to a close Scaredy Cat shivered with cold as he peered through the window. He had hardly been out all day, and had no intention of going out again. As the storm continued, he heard the sound of distant thunder, and realised that a thunderstorm was developing. It had been a terrible day's weather.

Scaredy Cat curled up on his bed in the warm kitchen, and decided to go to sleep during the evening. Mr Brown and his wife had only just come in from the driving rain and gusts of wind, and were now huddling round the fire, with the children, trying to get warm and dry. No one wanted to go out again that night, and the children settled down to do their homework.

After a while Mrs Brown went into the kitchen, switched on the light, and prepared to cook their meal. Scaredy Cat as usual, grew more interested. The rain continued to lash down, and the thunder grew ever closer to the vicarage, with occasional flashes of lightning. Scaredy Cat wondered what made it do that. He had heard Mr Brown say that on the television they had promised that it would happen later on, but Scaredy Cat still thought about who made it thunder, and flash with lightning. He realised that if God his Father made all things, then he controlled the weather also. God must have enormous power to do that, he imagined.

Just then there was a particularly bright and long flash of lightning. Scaredy Cat could see it quite clearly. It made the kitchen light up, and was followed by an enormous clap of thunder, which seemed to rumble on for ever. The old vicarage seemed to shake with it. 'My word,' said Mrs Brown, 'that must have been very close to us. I do hope that nobody has been hurt by the lightning.'

Suddenly, another bright flash of lightning lit up the whole sky. It seemed to Scaredy Cat that it happened right overhead. Then, to Scaredy Cat's surprise, total darkness! All the lights in the vicarage suddenly flickered and then went off, and Mrs Brown's electric cooker also stopped working. The electric clock in the kitchen stopped ticking away, and the whole place was now dark and gloomy.

Mrs Brown wailed, 'Oh dear, now what shall we do? That flash of lightning must have struck the power station. And all the power has gone. What's even worse, we can't see at all, and I cannot cook the supper.'

'No supper?' thought Scaredy Cat. 'No food? This calls for emergency action!'

At that point Mr Brown came into the kitchen, stumbling over the stool, and Scaredy Cat's box. The poor man could not see a thing. 'I wonder how long it will be before the power comes back on,' he said. 'This shows us how dependent we are on our electricity supply!'

Mrs Brown said, 'We can do something to help ourselves. If I can find where I put them, we can light a few candles. At least that will give us a bit of light to see us round the house.'

She fumbled around in the cupboard underneath the sink unit, but as she couldn't see a thing she failed to find them. Scaredy Cat thought. The loss of the light didn't worry him, because he could see in the dark, but the loss of his supper did. He wandered over to where Mrs Brown still rummaged in the cupboard for the candles. He could see them quite clearly. He pushed past Mrs Brown who was on her knees, still searching. 'Oh, Scaredy Cat,' she said, 'don't get in the way or I'll never find them!'

Scaredy Cat let her hands touch his back, and then he moved forward towards the box of candles. As Mrs Brown moved forward with him, her fingers touched the box. 'Oh, there they are!' she exclaimed. 'Scaredy Cat, you guided me towards the right place. You're a good boy!'

She handed the candles to Mr Brown, who began to light them, and stick them on some saucers. Soon they had lit enough to give quite a lot of light in the kitchen. Now Mrs Brown could make some food ready for their supper even though it had to be cold. Scaredy Cat felt that things were now getting better.

It was some two hours or more later before the lights came back on in the vicarage. The power had been restored, and all was well again. All this made Scaredy Cat think. 'People aren't very clever,' he decided. 'They can't see in the dark at all, and when the light goes out like that, they are lost because they can't see to do anything.'

Later on the next day, he discussed this matter with the

Stone Angel in church. 'Why can't people see in the dark?' he asked. 'I thought that people were much more clever than cats.'

'That's because not everybody has the same gifts,' replied the Stone Angel. 'Our Heavenly Father has given you the gift of seeing in the dark, while others have different gifts like singing, or being able to run fast or being able to make friends easily. We are all given different gifts, and we must use them to help others.'

'Oh, I see,' said Scaredy Cat. 'But some people are very frightened of the dark. Why is that?'

'To many people the dark stands for what is wrong or evil. They cannot see in the dark, and so it frightens them. Some people cannot go to sleep in the dark, unless they have a light on. They forget that our Heavenly Father is always caring for them, and is always near them.'

'I understand that,' said Scaredy Cat. 'If he is with us all the time, then there is no need to be scared of the dark. The Bible says that even the darkness is just like the light to him, so he can see all things.'

'I couldn't put it better myself,' said the Stone Angel.

Think about . . .

What gifts do you have? How do you use them? Can your gifts help other people? How?

Pray about . . .

Dear God,
   thank you for the gifts
   you have given me.

Sometimes
   I don't think I have any,
   that I'm not very special.
But, God,
   everyone is special to you,
   aren't they?

That's why
   you made us all
   so different.

We all have different gifts,
   from playing music
   to listening to people.

Please God,
   help everyone
   to use their gifts
   in the right way.

Amen.

BULLY BIRD

Scaredy Cat learns how to deal with bullies.

Ginger Tom settled himself down under the bushes and quietly waited. For several days now he had been watching Scaredy Cat as he came in and out of the house. The fact was that Scaredy Cat only seemed to come out of the house when he felt he needed to, and he avoided Ginger Tom and all the other friends in and around their garden. Ginger Tom also knew that he had not been in the church to see his friend the Stone Angel for several days. 'What was going on?' he thought.

After a time his patience was rewarded. Scaredy Cat slowly stepped out of the back door of the vicarage, and sat and looked around him. After a time he slowly walked down the path towards some bushes near to where Ginger Tom also sat. Ginger Tom wondered what Scaredy Cat was going to do. Then just as he reached a point on the path near to a big conifer tree, Ginger Tom heard a bird squawking, and poor Scaredy Cat ran for his life back into the vicarage once more. He did not come out again.

This had been going on for days, and Ginger Tom decided that he must find out more about it. He stationed himself near the vicarage door one evening, for he had noticed that Scaredy Cat only seemed to want to come out in the dark. He was not wrong, for Scaredy Cat came slowly out of the door and sat in the dark near Ginger Tom. He seemed very nervous.

'Hello, Scaredy Cat,' said Ginger Tom.

Scaredy Cat nearly jumped out of his skin. 'Oh, it's you,' said Scaredy Cat, 'I simply didn't see you there. How are you?'

'I'm fine,' said Ginger Tom, 'but how are you? I hardly ever see you out these days, and you seem to be very nervous about something. Whatever is the matter?'

'I'm sorry,' said Scaredy Cat. 'but I'm having a terrible time at the moment. I just don't know what to do about it, and it's making me feel very worried.'

'Whatever is the trouble?' asked Ginger Tom. 'Tell me about it, because that's what friends are for.'

'Well,' said Scaredy Cat, 'I'm very frightened. It's safe now, out here, in the dark, but I daren't go out in the daylight for fear of being seen.'

Ginger Tom stared at Scaredy Cat. 'What's going on? What on earth has made you so frightened? Have you seen something terrible? Has a mouse been trying to scare you off?'

'Not exactly. Well, not a mouse,' replied Scaredy Cat. 'In fact it's a bird!'

'A bird?' repeated Ginger Tom. 'I think you'll have to explain yourself. Afraid of a bird? What bird?'

'A few days ago,' replied Scaredy Cat, 'I expect you noticed that a family of crows came to nest in the conifer tree halfway down the garden.'

'Yes, I know,' said Ginger Tom. 'Great big black brutes that scream at you at the top of their voices; great ugly noisy things.'

'Yes,' said Scaredy Cat, 'that's them. Well the other day I was sleeping down the bottom of the garden when one of them landed quite near to me and began to create a terrible din. I wondered why it was so noisy at first, and then I realised that by my feet were a few red berries, which it obviously wanted. Suddenly this great bird flew at me and tried to peck me and drive me away. Well, he succeeded, and I fled into the house. I thought that was that, but the next day it did the same thing again. Now, every time it sees me it attacks me, so now I dare not go out in the day unless I keep close to the kitchen door. What shall I do?'

'Oh dear,' said Ginger Tom, 'you have got a problem. These old crows can be real bullies when they want to. and you are still only a small cat. No, I speak wrongly. I said you have a problem, but we must face this together as old friends. We have a problem, and we shall lick this between us. Let's go and talk to the Stone Angel and ask him what to do.'

Together, the two cats went into the church and sat in front of the Stone Angel and poured out their tale of woe and asked the Stone Angel for his advice.

'Well,' said the Stone Angel, 'the first thing is a point you have already agreed upon. Stay together with a friend. Help each other out. Bullies are really cowards, and if you stand up against them together they will not be so likely to start their bullying tactics again. A second thing is that you can try to keep out of the crow's way. If they don't see you they can't harm you. They sometimes forget quite quickly. Then you can always try the line of resisting them; if you stand up to them and refuse to run away, they won't have a clue what to do, and their attack will simply disappear. They can't handle what they don't understand. And, above all, don't forget to keep on praying; if you tell our Heavenly Father about the problem, and trust him to give you an answer, He will do something about it.'

The two cats returned home discussing what the Stone Angel had said to them. The next day they arranged to meet outside the vicarage door together. The crows flew over their heads calling and screaming as before, but the two friends ignored them. One of them dived towards Scaredy Cat, but Scaredy Cat moved suddenly and the crow missed him. Ginger Tom snarled at the crow who flew quickly away. The Stone Angel had been right: stand up to them and they soon give up the fight.

A few days later Scaredy Cat went to see the Stone Angel and report on the state of the matter. 'You were right,' said Scaredy Cat. 'Once we showed them that we were not to be pushed around, they soon gave up and now they keep out of our way.'

'Good,' said the Stone Angel. 'And don't forget the important point of prayer. Your Heavenly Father knows what the situation is and will help you, but you must learn to trust him, and tell him all about it!'

'I know!' said Scaredy Cat. 'Talking to him about everything is the best answer of all.'

Think about . . .

Sometimes you can come up against things which you can't face on your own and you need someone's help. Can you think of a time when this may happen?

Pray about . . .

Dear God,
    I know
    that I can't do everything
    on my own.

Sometimes I need the help
    of other people.

Sometimes it is school work,
    and other times
    it is more difficult,
    like standing up to someone.

Help me, God,
    to accept people's help
    and at the same time
    help others
    who may need me.

Amen.

THE VET

Scaredy Cat learns about the amazing variety of God's creation.

One morning Scaredy Cat crept slowly and miserably into church and sat down to talk to his friend the Stone Angel. He miaowed rather pitifully, and had no cheerful grin on his face as usual. 'Whatever is the matter?' asked the Stone Angel.

'I don't really know,' replied Scaredy Cat, 'but I don't feel very well. I seem to ache all over my body, my head aches, my eyes keep running and my nose is all stuffed up. I've been like this for two days now, so Mrs Brown is going to take me to the vet this afternoon. What is a vet?' he asked.

'A vet,' said the Stone Angel, 'is like a doctor, but they treat animals and birds and fish instead of people. When you go to see the vet he will soon be able to tell you what's wrong, and he will give you some medicine to take, and you will soon feel better again.'

'Well, I hope it works quickly, because I don't feel as if I will live much longer!' replied Scaredy Cat.

Later that day Scaredy Cat was wrapped up in a warm blanket, placed in a kind of basket, and taken by Mrs Brown to the vet. Scaredy Cat was quite surprised when he got inside. They went into a large room with chairs all round, and many people were sitting there. They would have a long wait, he thought. Everybody sitting on the chairs had some kind of creature with them. Scaredy Cat had never seen so many different things before.

There were many dogs, some very large and fierce looking, while others were quite small, even smaller than himself. Some had long hair and some had short hair, and in different

115

kinds of colours. There were many people with cats like himself. Some had jars and bowls with fish swimming around in them, and one man had a large snake in the corner. This worried Scaredy Cat who thought he might be eaten! One little girl had a box of mice, and another boy had a hen sitting in a cage.

On one side sat a lady with a bird cage on her knees, and when Scaredy Cat looked hard he saw a beautifully coloured parrot sitting in it. Another had some budgerigars in a small cage, all coloured green and blue. The noise the animals and birds made was deafening, with the barks and miaows and the chattering of birds. Scaredy Cat felt like putting his paws over his ears as they made his poor head ache even more.

One thing all the animals and other creatures had in common was that they all looked very sad and poorly. Then Scaredy Cat realised that they all had something the matter with them. He was not the only poorly puss in the world!

As Scaredy Cat thought about all this he realised what Mr Brown meant when he sometimes spoke of God's wonderful creation. There were so many different kinds of animals and birds, yet all had been made by God Himself. Certainly God did some wonderful things.

Before very long it was their turn to go to see the vet in another room. Mrs Brown took Scaredy Cat out of the basket and unwrapped the blanket. He found himself on a long table which smelled of disinfectant, and the vet, a kind looking woman, stood at one end. There was also a nurse who smiled sweetly at Scaredy Cat. 'What a lovely cat you've got,' she said. This made Scaredy Cat feel a lot better!

The vet picked him up gently and examined him very carefully. She took Scaredy Cat's temperature, and looked in his eyes, his mouth and his ears. Although she was very gentle, Scaredy Cat didn't enjoy this very much. Then she suddenly turned to Mrs Brown and said, 'I'm afraid that he's got cat flu!'

'What's she talking about?' thought Scaredy Cat. 'I haven't flown anywhere before!' As he continued to listen to the vet he realised he had caught a sort of very bad cold. 'Keep him indoors for a few days in the warm, and I'll give you a few powders to put into his food. I'll also give him an injection,' said the vet. Scaredy Cat didn't like the sound of all that, but it wasn't too bad. The vet found an instrument with a needle at one end, which she filled with some liquid. Then she gently prodded Scaredy Cat's back leg with it, and in a second it was all over. Scaredy Cat hardly felt a thing.

Back home, Scaredy Cat went into his basket under the kitchen table. 'It hasn't worked,' he thought. 'I still feel awful even after the visit to the vet!' Soon he was fast asleep, and for the next two days he never moved from the kitchen. He slept a lot, and only woke up to eat and drink. Mrs Brown had put the powders into his meal, but Scaredy Cat hardly noticed. He just ate and slept.

After two days Scaredy Cat woke up early in the morning, and decided that he felt a little better. His headache had gone and his body no longer ached so much, though he felt very stiff. Slowly during the next few days he began to feel better again. He felt more like running around again, and even wanted to go outside, if only to see his friend the Stone Angel.

One morning he was allowed out for a short time. He strolled up the church path and into the church, and sat down in his usual place.

'Good morning, Scaredy Cat,' said the Stone Angel. 'You do look much better than the last time I saw you. I have missed you and was rather worried about how you felt.'

'Oh,' said Scaredy Cat, 'I feel much better now. The vet said that I had cat flu or something. She gave me some powders to take and an injection with a huge needle,' he exaggerated. He then told the Stone Angel of all the events of the last few days.

'What surprised me,' continued Scaredy Cat, 'was the large number of different kinds of animals and birds there are in the world. They all looked sad and miserable.'

'Well, I expect that they all felt rather poorly,' said the Stone Angel. 'After all, that's why they had been taken to see the vet. As you met so many other animals, it reminds me that they all need to know about the Lord Jesus and his love for them as well as for you. Did you say anything to any of them?'

'Well, no,' said Scaredy Cat, 'I didn't have the time. You are right though. I must try and tell others of how God loves them so much. After all he made all of us.'

Think about . . .

Have you ever just sat and thought about how great God's creation is? Just think about all the different creatures and plants and places! Isn't it amazing!

Pray about . . .

Dear God,
    I'd just like to say
    that I think
    this world
    is brilliant!

It is so full
    of surprises,
    and sights,
    and smells,
    and tastes,
    and experiences,
    and much more!

And I live here!
That's brilliant too!

I know, God,
    that the world
    is not being looked after very well.
But I will do my best
    to help.

I love it here, God!
Thank you!

Amen.

CHOIR PRACTICE

Scaredy Cat learns how to show he is happy.

Scaredy Cat had been to choir practice. Each week the members of the church choir met to practise the hymns and other items of music that they would sing the following Sunday, and Scaredy Cat often sat and listened to them with a great deal of pleasure. After it was all over he sat talking to his friend the Stone Angel.

'Why do people sing?' he asked the Stone Angel.

'Well,' said the Stone Angel, 'people often enjoy singing, and it gives them a great deal of pleasure. Other people often enjoy listening to them also, either singing on their own as soloists or in a large group which we call a choir.'

'Why,' replied Scaredy Cat, 'do people sing a lot in church then?'

'For the same reasons,' said the Stone Angel. They also do it because the words and music say how they really feel about things. They sing because they are full of joy and happiness, as Christians often are. They sing also to say thank you to God for all he does for them.'

'Well I enjoy singing too!' said Scaredy Cat, 'but I don't think that many people enjoy my singing very much. One lady in church always tells me to be quiet when I start!'

'Sometimes you begin to sing when everybody else is trying to be quiet and listen!' exclaimed the Stone Angel. 'I also think you may need to sing a bit more in tune – I've heard you!'

'But I feel happy, and I want everybody else to feel happy too,' exclaimed Scaredy Cat. 'I want to sing to my Heavenly Father also, and tell him how much I love him.'

'Yes,' said the Stone Angel, 'but if I were you I'd try to do it a little more quietly than you usually do!'

Scaredy Cat went out of the church thinking hard about these things. He wanted everybody to know how happy he was and he wanted to share that happiness with everybody else. How could he show to everybody that he loved God when no one else could understand him?

Later that day Scaredy Cat met Ginger Tom, and they talked about the art of singing. Ginger Tom liked singing too, although Scaredy Cat thought that he couldn't sing as well as he did. The two cats talked on, and they both felt that they ought to tell everybody how well they could sing and how much they loved God.

'I know,' said Ginger Tom. 'It's been ages since I had a night out on the tiles. How about us both going out tonight when everybody has gone to bed, and serenading them with our beautiful voices! Perhaps they will want to join in with us as well!'

Scaredy Cat thought that it was an excellent idea, especially as he himself hadn't been out at night for quite a long time either.

That night, when all was dark and still and everybody seemed to be asleep, the two cats went out on the prowl. They went round their own gardens, and over the fences and walls, and watched the hidden night life, with other cats and mice and other animals creeping about, which humans knew nothing about. Being cats they could see clearly in the dark as if it were daytime.

Sitting on someone's front wall, the two cats tuned up their voices, and then began to sing. 'MIAOW!' they both chorused together, and then running up and down their singing scales, they sang as sweetly as they knew how at the top of their voices.

Suddenly they realised that they had been heard, and that someone was interested. Several lights were switched on in the bedrooms and people listened in great pleasure to their song! They began another song, and one or two windows were opened so that the people could listen more clearly to their beautiful voices. 'MMMIAAOWW!' they warbled in unison.

Then they heard it! Someone was shouting at them! 'Stop that racket now or I'll come and skin you,' shouted one voice.

Another yelled, 'Scram or else . . .' The two cats couldn't understand what all the fuss was about. Surely the people could hear them. Perhaps they needed to sing a bit louder, so they started up again.

Then it happened. At first one, then two then three shoes came whizzing through the air in their direction from various windows, followed by more shouts and howls. Luckily the people throwing were not very accurate!

Then they heard another window open just behind them, and suddenly a bucket of water came pouring towards the two cats. Scaredy Cat dodged it just in time, but poor Ginger Tom got his tail soaked. Moments later another bucket of water came through the air, and this time Scaredy Cat was not quick enough. He sat on the wall drenched to his skin.

The two cats could not understand it. They decided to go home and try to dry themselves out before the morning. As they crept home, the noise and commotion seemed to die down and all was quiet and still once more.

Next morning Scaredy Cat talked about this to his friend the Stone Angel. 'They certainly didn't seem to appreciate your singing,' said the Stone Angel with a smile, 'but don't give up so easily! Remember what the Bible says: "sing and make music in your hearts to the Lord", although it doesn't actually say anything about being in tune!'

Think about . . .

Do you ever want to do something really crazy because you feel so happy, even though you know others may think you're being silly?

Pray about . . .

Dear God,
 sometimes when I'm at church
 I want to run around
 and jump, and dance,
 because I feel so happy!

But I know that others will look at me
 as though there is something wrong.

And sometimes,
 I want to roll around in the grass
 and jump on my bed
 or yell and laugh really loudly,
 even though my parents
 might not want me to!

You don't mind, do you God?
 I'm just being happy.
And sometimes I need to show it.

Perhaps we should all
 show our happiness
 a little more?

Help us to, God.

Amen.

THE GARDENER

*Scaredy Cat learns that the process of growing
is quite a long, slow process.*

Scaredy Cat enjoyed gardening; at least his kind of gardening. He liked the garden because there were long stretches of grass on which he could run around and get plenty of exercise. He also liked trees which he could climb, bushes often with pretty flowers under which he could hide himself, and beautiful flowers which gave a lovely scent when he buried his nose in them. He didn't know much about the different kinds of flowers and plants, except the rose which had rather nasty thorns on it, but he always enjoyed watching Mr and Mrs Brown working in the garden, when they had a little time to give to it. It always seemed like hard work to Scaredy Cat, but he was getting to know more and more about it each week.

One day he watched with great interest. Mr Brown had bought some new plants; tiny things they seemed to Scaredy Cat. Now he was in the garden digging small holes in different places, and carefully planting the new flowers. As he worked, Mr Brown explained some things about gardening to Scaredy Cat, although he didn't realise how much Scaredy Cat could understand him.

'You see,' he said, 'each plant has to have a good root,' and he showed Scaredy Cat the long web-like roots, which he handled carefully. 'This is the part of the plant which must be buried into the ground. You must spread out the roots as much as possible, and be very careful that you do not damage or break them at all. Then, when the plant is settled into the soil, the roots will be able to suck up the water and all the food from the soil that it needs. This will help the little plant to grow big and strong.'

Scaredy Cat was very interested. He watched Mr Brown spread out the web of roots in the ground, and pile up the soil round the little plant. Then he pushed the soil onto the roots so that the little plants were firmly buried into the soil and wouldn't blow away. Finally he gave each plant a drink of water to help it settle down and grow. Scaredy Cat still remained very interested. He didn't think that he could put in the plants, but he would keep an eye on them and help them to grow.

As Scaredy Cat wandered round the rest of the garden he imagined how all the plants and trees and bushes had started life in this way. The trees must have looked very funny if they were only tiny plants, and he tried to imagine what they had looked like when they were only a few centimetres tall. At the end of the day he went indoors for his supper, well satisfied with his day's work, and looking forward to telling his friend the Stone Angel all about it the next day. He was sure that the Stone Angel didn't know as much about growing plants as he did, and he would tell him all about this.

A few days later Scaredy Cat went into the garden to inspect everything in it. Yes, all the trees and shrubs were still there and looking as fine as ever. He cast his eye over the plants, and saw the new ones that Mr Brown had planted last week. They were still there, none had fallen over or blown away. But then he stared harder at each little new plant. Surely there was something wrong!

As he inspected them, Scaredy Cat could see that each little new plant looked exactly as it did the other day when it had first been put into the ground. There were still no flowers on them, and they didn't seem to have grown at all. They were just the same height as before.

Scaredy Cat puzzled over this for a long time. He remembered Mr Brown saying that the root must not be damaged or the plant will not grow, indeed it might die. The plants didn't look as if they were dying, but they did not look as if they were growing either! Something must be very wrong. After thinking about this for a few more minutes, Scaredy Cat decided that he must do something about this. If the roots of the plants had been damaged, he must tell Mr Brown. But Mr Brown would not be able to understand him at all.

Scaredy Cat knew that there was only one thing he could do about this. If he dug up the plants, and laid them on the ground, Mr Brown could see that there was something wrong with the roots, and try to put it right. He would be very pleased with Scaredy Cat.

Scaredy Cat got to work. The first plant he came to, he began to scratch at the soil, and before long the plant became loose, and then finally lay on the ground with its roots showing. Scaredy Cat couldn't see anything wrong with them, but he thought that Mr Brown would when he saw it.

He carried on working until all twelve plants had been neatly scratched up and lay on the ground with their roots pointing into the sky. 'There,' thought Scaredy Cat, 'now all will be well.' He felt satisfied with his day's work.

Moments later he heard a shout and saw Mr Brown come running down the garden path. Mr Brown was not very pleased! Scaredy Cat tried to explain to Mr Brown what he had done, but Mr Brown did not seem to understand! Scaredy Cat was in trouble again. Mr Brown shouted at Scaredy Cat and then began to put all the plants back into the soil. He didn't seem very grateful.

Scaredy Cat explained it all to the Stone Angel the next day. He felt rather miserable, as he had lost his breakfast again, and had been told not to go into the garden for the rest of the week. He had been misunderstood, he said.

The Stone Angel listened quietly while Scaredy Cat poured out his woes. 'Sometimes people misunderstand what we say or do, even though we have the best of intentions in mind,' he said. 'After all, Jesus was not understood by many people, and they put him to death because of that.'

'Oh dear,' thought Scaredy Cat. 'I hope it doesn't go that far!'

'You simply didn't understand,' said the Stone Angel. 'Plants grow very slowly. After a week or so you can rarely see much difference in them, although they are really growing all the time. The roots are very important to them. Just like all Christians.'

'What do you mean?' asked Scaredy Cat.

'Just like the plant, Christians have to have a root also. That root is the way they take up their food and all the nourishment they need. The root is called prayer and Bible reading and worship. In this way, after a long time, young Christians also grow into strong Christians, wanting to love and serve their Heavenly Father.'

'It must take a long time,' said Scaredy Cat, 'but I think I see how it all works eventually.'

Think about . . .

Plants put down roots that help them grow. What type of roots do you think Christians need to help them grow?

Pray about . . .

Dear God,
   what type of roots
   do I need to grow?

I need food
   and water
   because they help me to grow.

I need family
   and friends
   because they love me
   and care for me.

I need school
   and church
   because that helps me
   to learn about
   so many things.

But I need other things.
I need to talk to you,
   and read about you,
   and learn about you.

These are my roots.

Help me to grow, God.

Amen.

THIEF

Scaredy Cat learns how to deal with temptation and that he must not steal things.

Mrs Brown had been busy in the kitchen of the vicarage nearly all morning. There was to be a kind of a celebration in the church hall at the end of the week, and she had been making cakes for the event, mixing all the ingredients, and putting them in the oven to cook. The kitchen was warm, and full of delicious smells that made Scaredy Cat feel particularly hungry. It seemed hours and hours since he'd had his breakfast, although it was still only the morning. He sat in his basket under the big table in the kitchen, his mouth watering, hoping for some titbits. None came his way. He rubbed around the legs of Mrs Brown hopefully, reminding her that he was there, but it seemed to make no difference. He just had to wait. 'Now,' said Mrs Brown, 'I must put out the fish from the freezer or there'll be nothing for supper tonight.'

Fish! Scaredy Cat could hardly believe his ears. Of all the food that he enjoyed, fish was surely the best. He waited till Mrs Brown went out of the kitchen and returned a few minutes later with the wet, frozen fish. Fish was the best thing in the world, he decided.

Mrs Brown went on doing jobs around the kitchen, but Scaredy Cat ignored her. He could think of only one thing – fish. 'Now Scaredy Cat, I'm going round to the church hall with all these cakes,' said Mrs Brown. 'I don't expect I'll be long. Just you make sure that you behave yourself while I'm away. We will have fish tonight, so I'll start to cook yours later this afternoon. Then it will cool down nicely for you.'

Scaredy Cat sighed. He had something to look forward to; some fish for his supper. Then he began to think. Why did Mrs Brown want to cook it first? He could eat the fish raw, not cooked. After all, most cats liked fish, and it didn't usually matter whether it had been cooked or not. Then, he thought, it seemed like two or three days since he had eaten last, perhaps they've started to starve me. Scaredy Cat decided that he ought to behave, so he stayed where he was. After some time having had a snooze and woken up again, he wondered why Mrs Brown was so long away. Perhaps she had been delayed or she wasn't going to come back home at all. Then he thought that if she didn't return soon, the fish might begin to go bad, and he knew that it would not keep for too long. The more he thought about it, the more his mouth watered again. The temptation was proving very strong.

Scaredy Cat got up and wandered around the kitchen. The place no longer seemed very interesting any more, all he could do was to think about that fish on the plate, sitting on the kitchen worktop. Perhaps it would be better if he climbed up and just took a look to see if it was all right – he could inspect it, and make sure that all was well.

He leaped up onto the kitchen chair, and then onto the worktop. All was clean and tidy, with nothing in the way, and there, at the end, was the plate with the fish lying on it. He slowly crept up to it, to inspect it; it looked all right. The fish were defrosting nicely, and there they lay, five beautifully thick white slices of fish, one for each person in the vicarage, and one for himself. They smelled marvellous.

Scaredy Cat sat and gazed at them, allowing the scent to wave past his nostrils. His tummy now felt very empty, and it began to rumble and roll in anticipation of the feast to come. Again Scaredy Cat began to think of the cooking. For the life of him, he couldn't see the point of going through all that long process, when he could eat it as it was. In fact, he thought, if he ate it, just his portion, it would save Mrs Brown the trouble of cooking it. That was it! She had been very busy, so he would save her some work by eating his piece now.

Scaredy Cat looked around. There was no sound and no sign of anybody about. He chose his own portion, the largest and the fattest of the five. He patted it carefully, to make sure that all was well, and then bent his head and began to tuck into the delicious fish. It was a bit cold still, and one or two bits were harder than he had expected, but that didn't matter. He just tucked into the fish, unaware of anything going on around him.

Just as he was consuming the last piece a voice screamed at him, 'Scaredy Cat! Just what do you think you are doing, you naughty cat? I forgot that I hadn't covered up that plate and that you could easily get at it.' Mrs Brown rushed over to the worktop, and picked him up. She dropped him onto the floor, and Scaredy Cat dived under the kitchen table. He knew just when and how to make himself disappear! He knew that he was in trouble again, and that he would get no more of the wonderful fish. Life seemed very difficult sometimes.

As he expected, he received a scolding, and the usual threat that he would have nothing more to eat that day.

He knew that he had been wrong, and that he should not have touched the fish, but the temptation proved too strong for him.

Later that day, he sought out his old friend the Stone Angel. He told him all about what he had done and the Stone Angel told him off very severely.

'As usual, Scaredy Cat, you forgot some very important things. First of all you stole the fish, and that you should never do. It is very wrong to take things that don't belong to you. I know that you only took what you would have had later, but that is not the point. You had no right to take them. They did not belong to you. Secondly, you kept on thinking about that fish. When you are tempted to do something wrong like that, you must learn to push the temptation away from you. Think of something quite different, and learn to resist the urge to do only what you want.'

'I know that you are right as usual,' said Scaredy Cat. 'I shall have to go and ask our Heavenly Father to forgive me again, and tell him that I am sorry. I wish I didn't have to keep doing this.'

'He will always go on forgiving you if you really mean it, because he loves you so. But you must also try much harder to do what is right. A Christian can find life very hard sometimes,' warned the Stone Angel.

Think about . . .

The kitchen is empty, and on the worktop are some nice
fresh chocolate buns. What do you do?

Pray about . . .

Dear God,
  what is stealing?

You see, sometimes
  if there's some nice food
  in the kitchen,
  and I know that I'll eat it later anyway,
  I want to just have a nibble,
  take a little cake,
  or stick my finger in the icing.

You see,
  I know it's naughty,
  but is it stealing?

I guess it is in some ways,
  because it's not for me to take
  but for someone else to give.

Help me, God,
  when this kind of thing happens,
  because I know it is wrong
  to take.

Give me patience, God.

Amen.

NETTED

Scaredy Cat learns the importance of not only helping others but also of working with others as a team.

Scaredy Cat and Ginger Tom were enjoying an afternoon's doze in the garden. With the sun warming their fur, and the birds singing, they lay down side by side, quietly contented, dreaming of their adventures of the day before. Life seemed very quiet and peaceful these days, and the two cats enjoyed each other's company. They had become good friends over the months, and often spent as much time as possible with each other. 'Life is very comfortable,' thought Scaredy Cat as he stretched out in the sun, without a worry in the world. Scaredy Cat was now growing up fast, though he was still quite thin. Ginger Tom had said that he was too active to grow fat, and in any case, Scaredy Cat didn't want to be plump. Yes, life was very good.

After some time the two cats woke up to the sound of the children's voices next door. It was the school holidays and the children were often playing outside in the garden during the day. The two cats wondered what today's game was, so they climbed the fence to look at next door and see what the noise was all about.

The children had found an old tennis net, which they had tied up between two trees across the lawn, and were playing a kind of tennis match. There were many shouts and giggles and hoots of laughter as the children enjoyed themselves with their make-shift game. The two children from the vicarage were there, and some of the others from across the road. Susan and David were opposite each other.

As usual, the children eventually grew tired 'of what they were doing, and just sat down on the lawn. Their stomachs were telling them that it was time to eat, so they all stood up and trooped indoors, leaving the garden quiet and still, with the net still hanging across the lawn. The two cats decided to investigate.

The net sagged badly in the middle, and sloped down till it nearly reached the ground at the centre, so with one on each side, the two cats began to play their own game. Ginger Tom tried to jump over the net, but he couldn't quite make it. Scaredy Cat knew he was still not quite big enough to try to jump over the net, so he decided to try and climb up the net, and over the top. Putting his front paws on the lowest parts of the mesh, Scaredy Cat heaved himself up. Then he tried putting his front paws further up the net, and bringing his back legs onto the net. Ever so slowly, Scaredy Cat went higher and higher up the net. Eventually he reached the top, though it was still not very far off the ground.

By clinging onto the net with his front paws, Scaredy Cat let go with his hind paws and tried to 'roll over' the top of the net. It was then that he ran into trouble. At first he couldn't get his body over the top of the net. Then all four paws got stuck in the top of the net. As soon as he managed to free one paw, the other paws became tangled. The more he lashed out to try to free himself, the more he became entangled, until he was soon hopelessly stuck! What could he do to free himself?

While all this was going on, Ginger Tom, who had run out of breath from his jumping, had sat on the lawn watching with his mouth open. Scaredy Cat did get himself into some scrapes sometimes, he thought. Then he realised that his friend was in such a mess that he needed help, but what could he possibly do to help him? He tried biting through one of the strings of the net to free one of his paws, but it was too tough, and didn't work.

Although it already sagged badly, he tried pulling the bottom of the net to the ground, but that didn't seem to work either. Ginger Tom sat down to think, while Scaredy Cat continued to thrash about on the net, making his position even worse than before. Suddenly Ginger Tom decided that there was only one thing that he could do; he must try to get some help from somebody, because it was obvious that they couldn't do it by themselves.

Ginger Tom went to the back door of the house. He sat down beside it and began to miaow as loudly as he could. 'MIAOW! MIAOW!' He made such a racket that soon one of the children, Susan Brown, opened the door to see what all the fuss was about.

She looked at Ginger Tom, who ran towards the net. Susan followed, and spotted Scaredy Cat still struggling to free himself from the net.

She ran to the net, and picked up Scaredy Cat, who still held onto the net with his claws. Susan had to prise his claws out of the net to free him, and then she set him down on the lawn.

Scaredy Cat sat on the ground for a moment, getting his breath back, as his little heart continued to go, 'thump, thump, thump!' Eventually he calmed down and began to look around. He had been rather foolish as usual. He saw now that it would have been impossible for him to climb up the net. His game had certainly ended for the day!

The next day Scaredy Cat met Ginger Tom in the garden, and they talked about their escapade of the day before. 'Thank you for helping me,' said Scaredy Cat to Ginger Tom. 'I was really stuck, and there was no way I could have got free unless you had helped me. It was just as the Stone Angel had said.'

'Oh,' said Ginger Tom, 'What did he say then? Did he have to tell you off again?'

'Well, he did say that I was silly,' admitted Scaredy Cat. 'He also pointed out that we had to work like a team in order to free me. He's right you know; we sometimes make a good team, you and I working together. That's how humans have to work, just like a team, even in a church. Each member has a job to do, and no one is more important than the other. They are all equally the same. Each has their own job to do.'

'I know,' said Ginger Tom. 'But I think that sometimes a lot of time is wasted arguing, especially when there are things to be done. If only humans lived and worked like us cats!'

Think about . . .

Think of a situation where you may need the help of others.
What do you need to be when working with others?

Pray about . . .

Dear God,
    sometimes
    there are things that I have to do
    where I need people to help me,
    or I need to help other people.

We have to work together.

It can be difficult,
    because you have to think
    of these other people.

You need to be patient,
    and listen to them.
You have to be helpful
    and willing to learn.

But it is so great
    when you work as a team
    and get it right!

I like that, God.
Thank you!

Amen.

CURIOSITY

Scaredy Cat learns that there are some very dangerous things in this world, and even curiosity should not tempt us to investigate them.

It is unlikely that Scaredy Cat had ever heard the old proverb, 'Curiosity killed the cat', but from his adventures it nearly happened.

Wandering around the front garden one day, Scaredy Cat heard the strangest noise; 'Squeak, squeak! Crunch, crunch! Bang, bang! Grind, grind! Scaredy Cat could hardly believe his ears. What on earth was making such a strange noise? He knew that somebody was working on the road outside the vicarage, he could hear their voices, but he could not understand exactly what was going on.

Curiosity overcame him. He didn't go outside onto the pavement very often, but today he just had to find out what was making all that noise. He walked down the drive and out onto the pavement, looking both ways to see what was happening. Some twenty yards further down the road were three men. They had put up a kind of tent over part of the footpath and seemed to be working inside it! They had huge rolls of cables, and they were unwinding one of these into a hole! As he listened to the men he realised that they were replacing some of the electric cables under the footpath, so they were unwinding the large rolls of cable, and pushing it down the hole.

Now Scaredy Cat had often seen the cover on the path, the 'manhole cover' he had heard it called, and had wondered exactly what was underneath it. Now he had a chance to find out. He quietly waited until the men went off for a cup of tea, and then he slowly wandered to the tent which was over the manhole.

He stepped carefully over all the cables and the strange tools and other things the men were using, and then stood on the edge of the hole. Looking down, he could see nothing.

The cables seemed to disappear into the hole, but where they went afterwards he could not see. It was far too dark, and the hole seemed to bend to one side, and so it became impossible to follow the cables. Scaredy Cat was consumed with curiosity. What exactly did the cables do, and where did they go? How long were they, and did they come up again from another hole further down the road? Did they make a noise, or did they smell? Were they attached to anything down below? Scaredy Cat simply had to know.

He caught a glimpse of something else down the hole, so he stood on tip-toe, and stretched his neck further down to try and have a better look. Then, suddenly, he felt himself slipping. He tried to grab at the side of the hole with his paws, but he failed.

He felt himself slipping down and falling and falling and brushing the rough sides of the hole, and banging his head on the cables. Then he landed, right at the bottom of the hole, amongst all the rubbish, the pipes and the cables which lay there.

He lay still trying to get his breath, wondering where he was. He could see in the dark, of course, but there didn't seem to be much to look at. The cables disappeared through another smaller hole, and there was little else to see now that he was down there. He didn't seem to have hurt himself at all, but when he looked up he could only just see the daylight through the top. It seemed a very long way up, and he knew that he wouldn't be able to climb back up the sides of the hole. He was stuck!

He began to panic. When would the men come back? Would they be able to rescue him? Would they be able to see him? Perhaps they had finished their job, and would come back and put the cover on the hole again. Then he would be shut in the hole for ever! So he did the only thing that he could think of, and yelled 'MIAOW!' as loudly as he could.

Then he stopped. As he miaowed he could hear his own voice over and over again. It sounded louder than he thought, and he could hear himself crying in an echo over and over again. Perhaps, with the noise, the men could hear him after all. Looking up he saw a face appear at the top of the hole.

'Here, Harry,' said the voice, 'I think we've caught a wild animal!'

'Well,' said another voice, 'it's making enough noise! It sounds like a cat. We'd better try and get him out I suppose, before we carry on laying these cables.'

To Scaredy Cat's surprise, one of the men seemed to be lowering himself down the hole. There was only just enough room for him to get down, so he blocked out most of the light. He seemed big and heavy and very clumsy. Scaredy Cat was sure that he could climb much better than that. Eventually the man reached the bottom of the hole. Scaredy Cat didn't hesitate, and jumped onto the man's trousers, digging in his claws to keep hold. The man yelled with surprise and pain, but Scaredy Cat ignored him, continuing to climb up the man until he reached his shoulders. Then he stopped.

The man was quite kind really, and gently stroked Scaredy Cat. 'How did you get down here?' he asked the little black and white cat, but of course Scaredy Cat couldn't tell him. Very slowly the man climbed back up the hole, until his head reached the top. Scaredy Cat jumped off his shoulder and right out of the hole, into fresh air and freedom once more. He turned to thank the man, but he just picked him up and dropped him over the wall, into the front garden of the vicarage. Scaredy Cat was safe once more, though rather dirty and shaken. He went back to his favourite spot in the garden to have a sleep and dream about his adventures.

'Curiosity nearly killed you,' said the Stone Angel to Scaredy Cat the next day.

'But how else will I learn about anything?' wailed Scaredy Cat.

'You could have asked me,' replied the Stone Angel. 'Many people have been hurt and even killed because they were curious, and didn't ask first. Railway lines or electricity cables are very dangerous things to play on, and you should never climb ladders'.

'Our Heavenly Father kept Daniel safe in the cave with all the lions. I heard the story about that the other day,' replied Scaredy Cat.

'I know,' said the Stone Angel, 'but he didn't deliberately go in there. He was forced into it by the soldiers. He didn't try to push his luck! You must remember that and not go into dangerous places, but avoid them!'

Think about . . .

It's fun finding out about things, and investigating things you've never seen or done before, isn't it? But can you think of a situation where it might be a bit silly to have a look?

Pray about . . .

Dear God,
    there is so much
    to see and do
    in this world,
    that I often find
    things I want to investigate,
    find out about
    and discover.

Sometimes though,
    this can be dangerous
    or a bit silly,
    as wanting to discover
    can become
    being nosy.

I know I won't go looking
    down a manhole
    like Scaredy Cat.
But, if there is something
    that I want to investigate
    that might get me into trouble,
    help me to realise this,
    and turn away.

Thanks, God.

Amen.

NAUGHTY DAYS

*Scaredy Cat learns that all Christians need to learn
how to behave, even on the bad days.*

It was washday. Scaredy Cat liked washday because the
kitchen was always warm, with loads of clothes waiting to
go into the washer all lying around the place. Sometimes
they smelled a bit funny, but Scaredy Cat ignored that
because they were heaped up in such a variety of lovely
bright colours. He liked playing with them, and making
nests on the clothes. He loved the steady chug-chug-chug
of the washer, and the steam when Mrs Brown opened the
door. Unfortunately it was not Mrs Brown's best day,
because she was always shooing him out of her way when
she was washing.

In the end Scaredy Cat went into the garden. Usually
on washdays it was raining, but not today. He looked up
at the washing-line, with all the clothes on it, wet but flap-
ping about in the breeze. Scaredy Cat watched; they
seemed to be in a playful mood today as they flapped one
way and then another, occasionally filled with the wind
which made them billow out and send them dancing.
They attracted Scaredy Cat's attention, and he sat and
watched them, fascinated. If only he could dance and play
like that!

Eventually he moved further on until he came to the
prop which held up the washing-line, stopping the cleaned
clothes dragging on the floor. He had an idea. 'Perhaps I
can dance like the clothes after all,' he thought. He sniffed
and tested the wooden prop, and decided.

Stretching himself up, he began to climb gingerly up
the prop to the washing-line. If he could climb far enough
up he might be able to catch the pillow case which was

the first item on the line nearest to the prop. Slowly he continued climbing up, higher and higher.

He did not look down because the prop was swaying with the wind. After some time he reached the top by the pillow case, now lying quite still. The wind had died down, and the pillow case, just hung there all limp, but inviting.

Scaredy Cat reached out and caught the pillow case with one paw. It moved slightly, so he dug his claws into it in order to hold on tightly. Then with a tremendous effort, he reached out his other paw and grasped the pillow case firmly with his two front paws. Just then, however, the wind began to blow fiercely, and Scaredy Cat felt the prop move under his back legs. The next moment the pillow case was swinging wildly in the breeze, with Scaredy Cat clinging on to it for dear life with his front paws.

Each time the pillow case swung, Scaredy Cat swung with it. He began to enjoy his ride! He was dancing with the washing high in the air, and not caring about the danger he was in, or the mess he was making with the pillow case. Suddenly Mrs Brown's voice came ringing in the air, 'Scaredy Cat! Just what do you think you are doing to my washing?'

Scaredy Cat looked down and for the first time realised the danger. Mrs Brown lowered the prop onto the ground, so that the washing line began to sag downwards. Then she grasped him round the body, and pulled him free from the pillow case. She dropped him onto the floor, and turned and scolded him roundly. 'Now I shall have to wash that pillow case all over again, thanks to you,' she said.

Scaredy Cat knew when he was in trouble, so he scooted back into the safety of the kitchen, and curled up in his box and dozed off to sleep. This was always the best way of dealing with a problem. He slept on until the middle of the afternoon, when he woke up and felt the need for some exercise. He turned to go outside but then found that the weather had changed and now it was raining quite hard. He hated getting wet so he turned round and went into the living room.

In getting ready for her weekly wash, Mrs Brown had decided to change all the cushion covers. She had bought some new ones, in bright reds and greens and golds, and Scaredy Cat decided to go and investigate them. He liked bright and cheerful things, so he decided to go and try out these cushions to see if they were as comfortable as the old ones. He sniffed round two of them. They seemed to be quite satisfactory. Then he turned his attention to the next one which was lying on a chair near to the door.

Looking to make sure that Mrs Brown was nowhere to be seen, he jumped up on the seat, a thing he was not allowed to do, and tried lying down on the cushion to see if it was warm and soft. Yes, he decided, that was quite in order also.

He came to the next cushion and plopped himself down rather heavily onto it. To his surprise the cushion seemed to groan and blow out quite a lot of air, and then suddenly a feather, only small, shot out of a corner which had not been stitched properly. Scaredy Cat watched it floating in the air, fascinated.

He quite liked the little feather and wondered if there were any more. He jumped on the cushion again, and this time two or three more feathers blew out and settled on the floor. This was great fun decided Scaredy Cat. He continued to jump up and down on the cushion, and each time he watched a long stream of feathers shooting out of the corner of the cushion. The more he jumped and the harder he landed, the more feathers came pouring out. He stopped to get his breath back again, and looked round. The whole room was now covered with feathers; the chair, the floor, all the furniture, and himself. Feathers were still swirling in the air. His own coat had now turned white with them. He had made a terrible mess. Scaredy Cat gazed round, quite pleased with what he had done.

Then Mrs Brown appeared in the doorway. Scaredy Cat did not stop to hear her words, but dived out through the open door. He ran down the garden path to put as much distance as he could between himself and the angry Mrs Brown. He crept under a bush, rain or no rain, and stayed there to keep out of the way until he felt that it was safe to return.

That night he slept again in the kitchen but this time with the door firmly closed so that he could not get out. He also slept with a very empty tummy, for, as usual, he had no supper. Mrs Brown's words on what she thought about him were still ringing in his ears!

The next day Scaredy Cat knew exactly what the Stone Angel would say to him. Yesterday he'd had a bad day, and been very naughty. The Stone Angel warned him that he must try harder. 'You must not go around unsettling other people just to please yourself,' he had said. 'We all have to make sacrifices for the sake of others. You wanted a bit of fun, and nobody blames you for that, but you must not bring harm or trouble to others. You must always let our Heavenly Father guide you. A Christian must always learn to behave.'

Think about . . .

It can be fun to be mischievous and a little bit naughty now and again, can't it? After all, everyone likes to jump up and down on their bed like a trampoline! But how do you feel when you have been found out?

Pray about . . .

Dear God,
    there are some things
    I like doing
    that I know I'm not allowed to.

Like jumping on my bed!
That's great fun!
But I know I shouldn't really do it.

It upsets my mum,
    and I don't mean to.

I just want to have some fun.

But there is a difference
    between having fun
    and being naughty.

Help me know it, God.

Amen.

Saying Hello

*How Scaredy Cat learns to work for his
Heavenly Father by helping others.*

The morning service was now over and the people were
beginning to go home. Soon the church was empty except
for two others. One of course, was the Stone Angel who
never went anywhere but just stayed where he was, listening
to others chatting, and continuing his job of praising God.
The other one was Scaredy Cat.

Scaredy Cat sat for a long time without moving and without saying anything. Eventually the Stone Angel spoke to
him. 'What's the matter, my friend? What are you thinking
about so deeply?'

'Well,' replied Scaredy Cat, 'I was thinking about what
Mr Brown had been saying in his sermon this morning.
He was talking about how we should work for our
Heavenly Father, and try to serve him by telling others
about him, and help them to know him better.' Then
Scaredy Cat sighed deeply. 'The trouble is, I just don't
know how I can do this. I can't tell them about our
Heavenly Father because people don't know what I am
saying. All they can hear is "Miaow". I can't tell them to
come to church to hear more about him, and I certainly
can't go into the streets and drag them in. Fancy a cat
dragging people into church!'

The Stone Angel chuckled as he thought about Scaredy
Cat grabbing people by the hand and pulling them through
the church door. Then he said slowly, 'Well, I see what
you mean. I think, however, that there is something that
you might do. You could encourage people to come into
church by making them more welcome. Many people like
a smile when they come in, and a warm handshake when

they are given their hymn books. Perhaps you could do something like that.'

Scaredy Cat stared at the Stone Angel. What on earth did the Stone Angel mean? He knew that if he smiled at people they usually backed away, and shaking hands was one thing that people were not keen to do with a cat. 'Still,' he thought, 'I might be able to do it in my own way.'

The next Sunday morning saw Scaredy Cat parked out-side the church door some time before the service was due to begin. As soon as he saw someone coming into the church, he went up to them and made friends with them. That didn't seem to work, but he greeted them with a loud 'miaow', and rubbed round their legs and feet to show them that he welcomed them.

The first person who came in was a tall man. As soon as Scaredy Cat rubbed round his feet, the man, rather bad-tempered, shooed him away, and ignored him. Scaredy Cat tried again. An elderly lady came along, and she greeted Scaredy Cat and stroked him before she went inside. This was better.

Scaredy Cat carried on with his welcoming act. Each person he miaowed to and greeted in one way or another by being friendly with them, and purring when they stroked him. There were a lot of people which meant a lot of purring and miaowing, but Scaredy Cat didn't mind. It was tiring but enjoyable work, and he felt that he was doing something very important.

Soon it was time for the service to begin. Scaredy Cat followed the last person into the church and sat in his usual place, listening to what was going on. He found the work very tiring, however, and before long he had dozed off to sleep. In fact he slept so long that he missed Mr Brown's sermon entirely, and only woke up during the last hymn. 'Dear me,' he thought, 'this work for our Heavenly Father is a rather tiring business, and I'm not at all sure that it was very successful.' He wondered if he had put people off coming into church instead of welcoming them.

At the end of the service, when Scaredy Cat was just going out of the church, he heard someone behind him say, 'Look! There's that cat again! At least he makes people feel cheerful and happy, even if no one else does!'

Later on, Scaredy Cat talked to his friend the Stone Angel all about this. 'I tried to do something, but I'm not sure if it worked very well,' he complained. 'There are some things that I'm simply not very good at.'

'Not at all,' replied the Stone Angel. 'It was good to see someone being friendly to others, and it is certainly cheering some of the people to see and hear you. It's easy to be miserable, and it's sometimes quite hard to be bright and cheerful. I'm sure that our Heavenly Father likes to see us all cheerful and happy and ready to welcome others. That's important for a Christian.'

Scaredy Cat thought about this. 'Well,' he thought, 'it is certainly hard work. I was tired after all this and a bit disappointed. Perhaps our Heavenly Father was pleased with me, even though some people weren't.'

As he went outside again, he saw some of the children playing games. He listened to their cheerful laughter and their chatting. Many of them had been in church and he had been able to greet them. They knew him well.

Suddenly one of them called attention to him. 'Hello, Scaredy Cat! Come and join us and play with us!' Scaredy Cat was surprised but trotted over to them. Soon he was playing skipping with them, jumping up and down over the rope that the children were using.

The children laughed and cheered at him, so he tried to do some simple tricks with the rope. He not only jumped over it, but he tried to climb up the end of it, and cling to it and swing on it. He quite enjoyed himself and the children certainly laughed at his antics.

Suddenly Scaredy Cat stopped and thought. 'These children were all in church today. In the church and outside it, I've been able to cheer them up and help them to enjoy themselves. Perhaps this is the way that I can help others and bring them into the services; I can play with them and help them to be happy.'

Later on he talked to the Stone Angel about all this. 'Just so,' said the Stone Angel. 'By being friendly and helping others to be cheerful and happy, you may have done much in helping them to remember all that our Heavenly Father has done for them. This is indeed a real work for him. And also it cheers you up!'

Think about . . .

Can you think of any ways you could let people know about God's love, like Scaredy Cat welcoming people into church?

Pray about . . .

Dear God,
    how can I show people
    your love?

You see,
    I know you love me
    and that you love everyone,
    but I want to help
    and show people
    how much you *do* love them!

I can do things
    like help people,
    and be friends with them.
I can he happy,
    and hug them!

Is that good enough, God?
Will that help?

I'll start right away!

Amen.

MEET THE FAMILY

*How Scaredy Cat learns that he belongs to
the world-wide family of God.*

'There! That's finished!' Mr Brown stood back to survey
his car now standing in the drive at the vicarage. He had
spent over an hour on it, washing it down with a hose-
pipe, and then drying it off and polishing it, and now it
stood there, gleaming and bright and looking very smart.
Scaredy Cat had been watching all these proceedings with
great interest from a distance. As it was a warm and sunny
day, Mr Brown left the doors of his car wide open so that
the air could blow through it. He was very pleased with
his work.

When Mr Brown had gone back inside, Scaredy Cat
went to inspect the car. He walked round it, sniffing at the
wheels and noted the smell of the polish. He made sure
that no oil or water was dripping from under the car, and
that Mr Brown had not missed any small patches. All
seemed well.

He then decided to climb into the car and check that
the inside was just as clean as the outside. The leather
seats of the old car also seemed to shine with polish, and
there was no trace of dust or dirt anywhere. Scaredy Cat
decided that it seemed to be a good place to settle down
to snooze in the warmth, so he sat down on one of the
cushions on the back seat, and was soon fast asleep.

He was suddenly woken up by a loud bang, or rather a
series of bangs. Mr Brown had come out of the Vicarage
front door, and without noticing Scaredy Cat he had
slammed shut three of the doors, and was climbing into
the driving seat himself. After a moment the engine roared
into life, and Mr Brown slowly drove out of the drive and

onto the road, being totally unaware that Scaredy Cat was still inside!

Scaredy Cat realised that he was now going to have to go for an unexpected ride. He didn't say anything, but just lay there on the back seat enjoying himself. Where was Mr Brown going to and how long would he be? Scaredy Cat watched with great interest as the houses and shops and factories seemed to fly past. He shook as other cars passed by them, some of them very noisily indeed.

Mr Brown seemed to be driving faster and faster all the time, and as they went round some narrow bends in the road, Scaredy Cat felt the car brake and he heard the tyres scream on the surface as they manoeuvred round the bends.

Soon they were in the country with fields and trees and hedges rushing past them. The roads were also much narrower and so other passing vehicles seemed to only just miss the car.

Finally, Scaredy Cat felt the car slowing down and turning off the road. When Scaredy Cat looked out, he saw that Mr Brown was pulling into a garage. He got out of the car and began to fill up with more petrol. Scaredy Cat heard the hum and whine of the petrol pump, and could smell the acidy smell of the petrol fumes. Still he lay quietly on the back seat, Mr Brown still not noticing him.

Mr Brown fumbled in his pockets for some money for the petrol, and went to pay the man in the kiosk. When he came back, he dropped something on the floor and went to pick it up. In straightening up again, he caught a glimpse of Scaredy Cat in the back seat of the car.

'Scaredy Cat! What on earth are you doing there?' he cried. 'Mrs Brown will be looking all over the place for you.' Then he thought for a minute. 'I suppose you crept into the car when I left the doors open, but I never spotted you till now.' Scaredy Cat miaowed happily. He had been having a great time and was thoroughly enjoying himself. He wondered where they were going to. 'Well, I've come too far now, you'll just have to stay with me.'

They started off again, and drove on for about another hour, still rushing through the countryside that Scaredy Cat had never seen before. He and Mr Brown chatted together for some time, but of course Mr Brown couldn't understand him at all. Then suddenly he said, 'You're going to meet another Mrs Brown now. This lady is quite old but she loves cats and you'll love her. This Mrs Brown is my mother.' Scaredy Cat was very surprised. Mr Brown having a mother? That was something he had never thought of before.

They finally arrived at a small house on the edge of a village. Mr Brown got out of the car and locked it up. Then he picked up Scaredy Cat and carried him to the front door. He knocked on the door and after a while the door opened and there stood a little old lady with a walking stick. She had white hair, almost like silver, and a cheery grin on her face. She greeted Mr Brown warmly, but when she saw Scaredy Cat she gave a cry of delight.

She talked to him and stroked him, and later on he sat on her lap while she cuddled him and loved him. While Mr Brown talked to his mother and explained why Scaredy Cat was travelling with him, Scaredy Cat noticed that the room was much smaller than those of the vicarage, but was warm and bright and cheerful.

The old lady gave him a saucer of milk and later on a little bit of fish to eat. How did she know just what Scaredy Cat liked best of all?

'So this is the famous Scaredy Cat, is it?' she said, stroking him. 'I've heard such a lot about you, and now I've met you!'

Scaredy Cat decided that he liked the old lady and her house, and that he could be very comfortable living there. As if reading his thoughts old Mrs Brown said, 'If ever my son wants to move, you can always come and live here. You and I would be good friends!'

Scaredy Cat agreed and smiled warmly to himself. Soon, almost too soon, however, it was time to go home. The journey home seemed long and tiring, and the weather at night grew quite cold. Scaredy Cat watched the lights from the houses which looked almost like ghosts with eyes in the night. Many cars rushed back and forth, looking like searchlights in the darkened sky. It was quite late when they arrived back home, with Mrs Brown looking very worried because she had not been able to find Scaredy Cat.

The next day, as soon as he could, Scaredy Cat trotted round to the church to talk once more to his friend the Stone Angel. He told him of all his exciting adventures of the day before, and how he had met the old Mrs Brown, Mr Brown's mother.

'We all belong to a family of some kind,' said the Stone Angel. 'You had a mother and a father and a family once, although no one knows who or where they are.'

'Perhaps they are very famous cats, like a king or a

queen!' replied Scaredy Cat, and then asked, 'Why are families so important?'

'It's a matter of belonging,' said the Stone Angel. 'When we belong to a family we belong to someone else, and it means that there is always someone to take care of us, and help and love us. Jesus had his own family for many years and so did many of the famous people we read of in the Bible.'

'Is that what Mr Brown means when he talks about the family of God?' asked Scaredy Cat.

'In a way, yes,' replied the Stone Angel. 'All Christians belong to another family, a great family of Christians. We all belong to one family and so care for each other, and help and support each other when we fall ill or are in trouble in any kind of way, or are in need of support or encouragement. That family is spread all over the world, and in every country there are Christians who all belong to the same family, although we can't always speak the same language. It is the worldwide family of God.'

'I suppose that is why God is over us all, for he is our Heavenly Father,' replied Scaredy Cat. 'Does this mean that I should give a birthday present to everybody?'

The Stone Angel looked down at Scaredy Cat and chuckled. 'He really has grown up into a fine cat,' he muttered to himself as Scaredy Cat wandered out of the church and into the sunshine. 'A fine cat indeed, and certainly not a Scaredy Cat!'

Think about . . .

Think about your worldwide family. Not just those you live with, or those who are your friends, but everyone. The people in faraway places like Australia and Africa! We are one big family! Isn't that great!

Pray about . . .

Dear God,
    I'm a part of a huge family,
    aren't I?

You know,
    not just here,
    or my friends,
    but everyone around the world!
We are a family!

That's amazing!
I wish we could all get on well, though.
There is so much sadness in the world,
    but there is a lot of happiness, too.

Help us, God,
    to spread the happiness around a bit.
Maybe then,
    we can be a worldwide
    happy family!

I hope so.

Amen.